2016-2018 OCCUPATIONAL PROGRAMS IN CALIFORNIA COMMUNITY COLLEGES

Published by
LAMA Books

ISBN 978-0-88069-087-4

2381 Sleepy Hollow Ave • Hayward CA 94545-3429
888-452-6244 • 510-785-1099 Fax • www.lamabooks.com • lama@lamabooks.com

FOREWORD

Previous editions of this directory have been evaluated by students and counselors as a most effective and convenient source of information about occupational programs in California community colleges. We hope that this current edition will continue to assist in selecting the community college and occupational programs most appropriate to the students' needs.

The 112 community colleges in California offer over 5000 different occupational programs. The designation of a "program" has been left to the judgment of each college. This 2016-2018 edition has been prepared so the up-to-date information on this wide variety of career opportunities is available to all educators and others.

TABLE OF CONTENTS

SECTION 1
General Information—California Community Colleges

Information concerning admission procedures, costs, and special services available.

SECTION 1
GENERAL INFORMATION ABOUT CALIFORNIA COMMUNITY COLLEGES

The community college in California provides several kinds of programs:

1. Occupational education programs (including upgrading courses for employed adults).
2. General education courses.
3. Transfer programs to the State Universities and to the University of California.
4. Community education programs.
5. Preservice for business and industry to prepare students for jobs.

Some community college districts have separate colleges within their boundaries. Some colleges have separate centers in different locations. Distance education is available at many colleges.

Some colleges are on the semester system; others are on the quarter system. Semesters usually begin in September and February. Quarters usually begin in September, January, and April.

Visit the web site www.cccco.edu and go to *Find a College* for information about the various community colleges.

ADMISSION REQUIREMENTS

To be admitted to a California community college, one must complete the registration procedures established by that college and meet **one** of the following qualifications:

1. Have a high school diploma or equivalent.
2. Be 18 years of age or older, and able to profit from instruction.

COSTS

California residents pay an enrollment fee per unit for the academic year. Fees vary for quarter and semester systems. Nonresidents (out of state and foreign students) pay tuition per unit for the academic year in addition to enrollment fees.

Students pay for textbooks. Additional fees may be charged, such as parking, health, and records processing fees. Financial aid is available, and every college has a financial aid office.

Contact the college of your choice for exact costs.

HOW TO APPLY

It is important to apply at least three months before classes start—preferably sooner. Contact the college Office of Admissions and Records for an application for admission. Many colleges accept applications on their web site. Visit web site www.cccapply.org for online application information.

Immediately after applying for admission, request in writing from all the high schools and colleges you have attended that transcripts of your records be sent to the college to which you are applying.

Students will be advised of matriculation activities required. These include orientation, assessment, and counseling.

STUDENT SERVICES

Most colleges provide:

- List of housing available in the community.
- Information and assistance regarding grants, loans, and scholarships.
- Educational and personal counseling.
- Assistance in obtaining employment both on and off campus.
- Special advice and assistance for veterans.
- Tutoring services for students with special needs.

Some community colleges maintain dormitories or college apartments. See the college pages in Section 3 for housing information.

FOREIGN STUDENTS

Foreign students may be admitted.

A Certificate of Eligibility for Student Visa (Form 1-20) is issued by the college admitting the student. The student must enroll in at least 12 semester credit units and maintain a 2.0 (C) grade average.

LENGTH OF PROGRAMS

Programs vary from one semester (or quarter) to two years.

Some programs are available exclusively in the evening and Saturdays. These may require a longer period of time to acquire a certificate or degree. Almost all colleges offer summer sessions.

SECTION 2
Program Location Charts

The charts show which colleges offer a type of occupational program. The programs are organized in the following categories:

- Agriculture
- Business and Office
- Communications
- Criminal Justice
- Electrical and Electronics
- Engineering and Technology
- Environment and Natural Resources
- Health Services
- Home Economics and Food Service
- Management and Supervision
- Science and Laboratory
- Service
- Trade and Industry

APPRENTICESHIP—Many community colleges offer apprenticeship classes for persons employed as indentured apprentices in construction and other apprenticeable trades. Apprenticeship classes are not included in this book.

AGRICULTURE

COLLEGES	Agriculture	Agri-Business	Agri-Engineering	Agri-Laboratory	Agri-Mechanics	Animal Husbandry	Animal Science	Artificial Insemination	Crop Production	Dairy Science	Floristry	Food Processing	Horticulture	Irrigation	Landscaping	Nursery Industry	Plant Science	Poultry Husbandry	Soil Technology	Sustainable Landscape	Tree Production and Care	Turf Management	Viticulture	Winery Technology						
Alameda																														
Allan Hancock		❖																					❖	❖						
American River											❖		❖		❖															
Antelope Valley	❖												❖		❖															
Bakersfield	❖	❖					❖						❖				❖													
Barstow																														
Berkeley City																														
Butte	❖	❖			❖				❖		❖		❖		❖							❖								
Cabrillo									❖				❖		❖	❖								❖						
Cañada																														
Canyons																							❖							
Cerritos																														
Cerro Coso																														
Chabot																														
Chaffey												❖																		
Citrus																														
Coastline																														
Columbia																														
Contra Costa																														
Copper Mountain																														
Cosumnes River	❖	❖					❖						❖	❖	❖	❖														
Crafton Hills																														
Cuesta	❖																													
Cuyamaca											❖		❖	❖	❖	❖						❖								
Cypress																														
De Anza																														
Desert	❖	❖											❖	❖	❖		❖			❖		❖								
Diablo Valley													❖		❖	❖				❖										
East Los Angeles																														
El Camino													❖																	
Evergreen Valley																														
Feather River	❖					❖	❖																							
Folsom Lake																														
Foothill													❖		❖															
Fresno City													❖																	
Fullerton													❖	❖	❖	❖	❖													
Gavilan																														
Glendale																														
Golden West											❖																			
Grossmont																														
Hartnell	❖	❖							❖			❖																		
Imperial Valley	❖	❖							❖																					
Irvine Valley																														
Lake Tahoe																														
Laney																														
Las Positas													❖										❖	❖						
Lassen	❖	❖					❖																							
Long Beach City											❖		❖																	
Los Angeles City																														
Los Angeles Harbor																														
Los Angeles Mission																														
Los Angeles Pierce	❖					❖	❖				❖		❖		❖															
Los Angeles Southwest																														
Los Angeles Trade-Technical																														
Los Angeles Valley																														
Los Medanos																														

AGRICULTURE

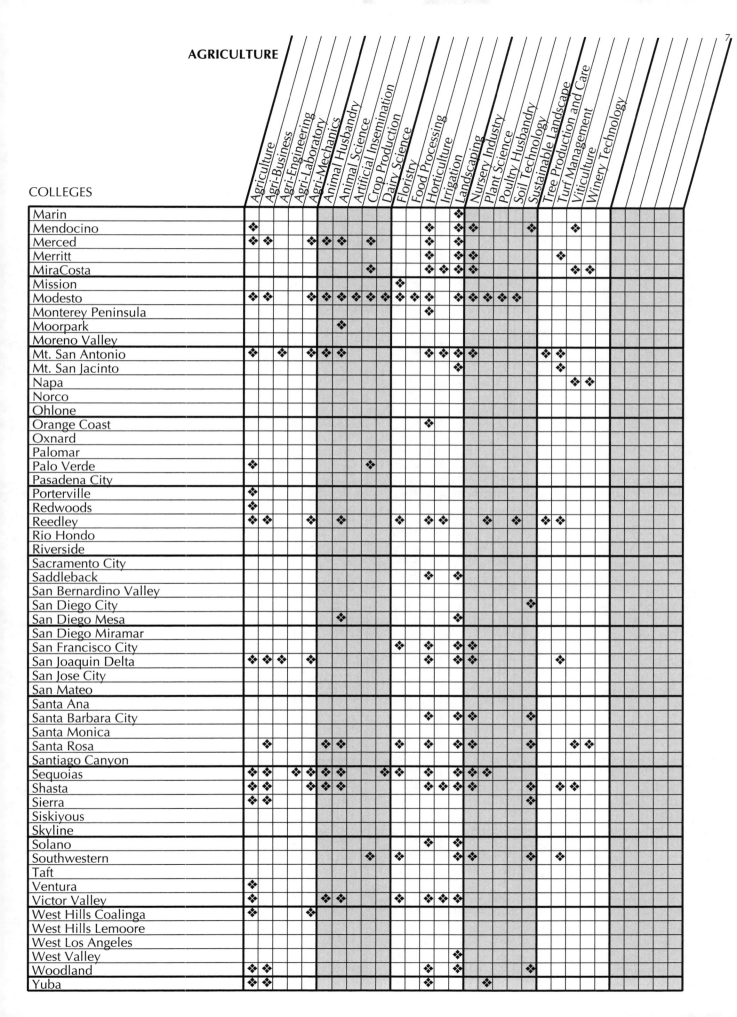

COLLEGES	Agriculture	Agri-Business	Agri-Engineering	Agri-Laboratory	Agri-Mechanics	Animal Husbandry	Animal Science	Artificial Insemination	Crop Production	Dairy Science	Floristry	Food Processing	Horticulture	Irrigation	Landscaping	Nursery Industry	Plant Science	Poultry Husbandry	Soil Technology	Sustainable Landscape	Tree Production and Care	Turf Management	Viticulture	Winery Technology
Marin															❖									
Mendocino	❖												❖		❖	❖				❖			❖	
Merced	❖	❖			❖	❖	❖		❖				❖		❖									
Merritt													❖		❖	❖						❖		
MiraCosta									❖				❖	❖	❖	❖							❖	❖
Mission											❖													
Modesto	❖	❖			❖	❖	❖	❖	❖	❖	❖	❖	❖		❖	❖	❖	❖	❖					
Monterey Peninsula													❖											
Moorpark							❖																	
Moreno Valley																								
Mt. San Antonio	❖		❖		❖	❖	❖						❖	❖	❖	❖					❖	❖		
Mt. San Jacinto															❖							❖		
Napa																							❖	❖
Norco																								
Ohlone																								
Orange Coast													❖											
Oxnard																								
Palomar																								
Palo Verde	❖								❖															
Pasadena City																								
Porterville	❖																							
Redwoods	❖																							
Reedley	❖	❖			❖		❖				❖		❖	❖			❖		❖		❖	❖		
Rio Hondo																								
Riverside																								
Sacramento City																								
Saddleback													❖		❖									
San Bernardino Valley																								
San Diego City																				❖				
San Diego Mesa							❖								❖									
San Diego Miramar																								
San Francisco City											❖		❖		❖	❖								
San Joaquin Delta	❖	❖	❖		❖								❖		❖	❖						❖		
San Jose City																								
San Mateo																								
Santa Ana																								
Santa Barbara City													❖		❖	❖				❖				
Santa Monica																								
Santa Rosa		❖				❖	❖				❖		❖		❖	❖				❖			❖	❖
Santiago Canyon																								
Sequoias	❖	❖		❖	❖	❖	❖			❖	❖		❖		❖	❖	❖							
Shasta	❖	❖			❖	❖	❖						❖	❖	❖	❖				❖		❖	❖	
Sierra	❖	❖																		❖				
Siskiyous																								
Skyline																								
Solano													❖		❖									
Southwestern									❖		❖				❖	❖				❖		❖		
Taft																								
Ventura	❖																							
Victor Valley	❖					❖	❖				❖		❖	❖	❖									
West Hills Coalinga	❖				❖																			
West Hills Lemoore																								
West Los Angeles																								
West Valley															❖									
Woodland	❖	❖											❖		❖					❖				
Yuba	❖	❖											❖				❖							

BUSINESS & OFFICE

COLLEGES	Accounting	Advertising	Banking & Finance	Business	Business Writing	Clerical	Computer Info Science (CIS)	Computer Networking	Court Reporting	Data Entry	E-Commerce	Entrepreneurship	Escrow	Insurance	International Business	Merchandising/Retail	Payroll Clerk	Product Design	Real Estate	Receptionist	Secretary	Secretary (bilingual)	Small Business	Tax Preparer	Transportation & Distribution	Word/Information Processing
Alameda	❖			❖		❖	❖									❖							❖		❖	❖
Allan Hancock	❖			❖			❖	❖				❖				❖							❖			❖
American River	❖	❖		❖		❖	❖	❖								❖			❖				❖	❖		
Antelope Valley				❖		❖	❖	❖											❖				❖			
Bakersfield	❖			❖		❖																				
Barstow	❖			❖			❖																		❖	
Berkeley City	❖			❖		❖	❖																			
Butte	❖			❖				❖								❖			❖					❖		
Cabrillo	❖			❖		❖	❖	❖																		
Cañada	❖			❖		❖										❖	❖						❖			
Canyons	❖		❖	❖			❖	❖			❖	❖			❖	❖			❖							
Cerritos	❖			❖		❖	❖	❖	❖			❖		❖	❖	❖	❖	❖	❖		❖		❖			❖
Cerro Coso				❖			❖					❖											❖			
Chabot	❖			❖		❖	❖					❖			❖	❖			❖		❖		❖			
Chaffey	❖		❖	❖		❖	❖			❖		❖				❖	❖					❖	❖	❖	❖	
Citrus				❖																						
Coastline	❖			❖	❖	❖		❖				❖				❖			❖				❖	❖	❖	
Columbia	❖					❖	❖	❖				❖					❖				❖		❖	❖		
Contra Costa	❖			❖		❖	❖	❖											❖							
Copper Mountain	❖			❖			❖																			
Cosumnes River	❖	❖	❖	❖		❖	❖	❖			❖	❖				❖			❖		❖		❖			
Crafton Hills				❖			❖	❖								❖										
Cuesta	❖			❖	❖	❖	❖	❖													❖					
Cuyamaca	❖			❖		❖	❖	❖				❖							❖	❖	❖		❖			
Cypress	❖	❖		❖		❖	❖	❖	❖					❖		❖					❖		❖			❖
De Anza	❖			❖		❖	❖	❖				❖							❖		❖			❖		
Desert	❖			❖			❖									❖									❖	
Diablo Valley	❖		❖	❖		❖	❖	❖				❖				❖			❖				❖			
East Los Angeles	❖			❖		❖	❖												❖		❖				❖	❖
ElCamino	❖			❖			❖									❖			❖							
Evergreen Valley	❖			❖								❖														❖
Feather River	❖		❖	❖		❖						❖									❖		❖			
Folsom Lake	❖			❖		❖	❖			❖		❖				❖			❖				❖			❖
Foothill	❖		❖			❖									❖		❖							❖		
Fresno City	❖	❖	❖	❖		❖	❖	❖		❖		❖	❖			❖			❖				❖		❖	
Fullerton	❖	❖		❖	❖	❖	❖	❖			❖	❖			❖	❖			❖				❖			❖
Gavilan	❖			❖		❖	❖	❖								❖			❖							
Glendale	❖		❖	❖		❖	❖					❖		❖	❖	❖			❖	❖	❖		❖	❖		
Golden West	❖											❖				❖					❖		❖	❖		
Grossmont	❖			❖		❖	❖	❖				❖		❖	❖	❖				❖	❖					
Hartnell				❖			❖	❖																		
Imperial Valley	❖		❖	❖		❖	❖	❖																		
Irvine Valley	❖		❖				❖	❖				❖				❖	❖		❖				❖	❖		
Lake Tahoe	❖			❖			❖																			
Laney	❖		❖	❖			❖					❖				❖										❖
Las Positas	❖			❖		❖	❖	❖				❖														
Lassen	❖			❖		❖						❖									❖					
Los Beach City	❖			❖				❖							❖	❖									❖	
Los Angeles City	❖		❖	❖		❖	❖	❖								❖			❖				❖			❖
Los Angeles Harbor	❖			❖		❖	❖												❖							
Los Angeles Mission	❖		❖	❖		❖	❖									❖										
Los Angeles Pierce	❖			❖		❖	❖	❖							❖	❖					❖		❖	❖		❖
Los Angeles Southwest	❖		❖	❖		❖	❖	❖				❖	❖						❖	❖	❖		❖	❖		❖
Los Angeles Trade-Technical	❖			❖		❖	❖	❖				❖				❖			❖				❖			
Los Angeles Valley	❖		❖	❖		❖	❖	❖											❖		❖					
Los Medanos	❖			❖			❖	❖								❖			❖				❖			

BUSINESS & OFFICE

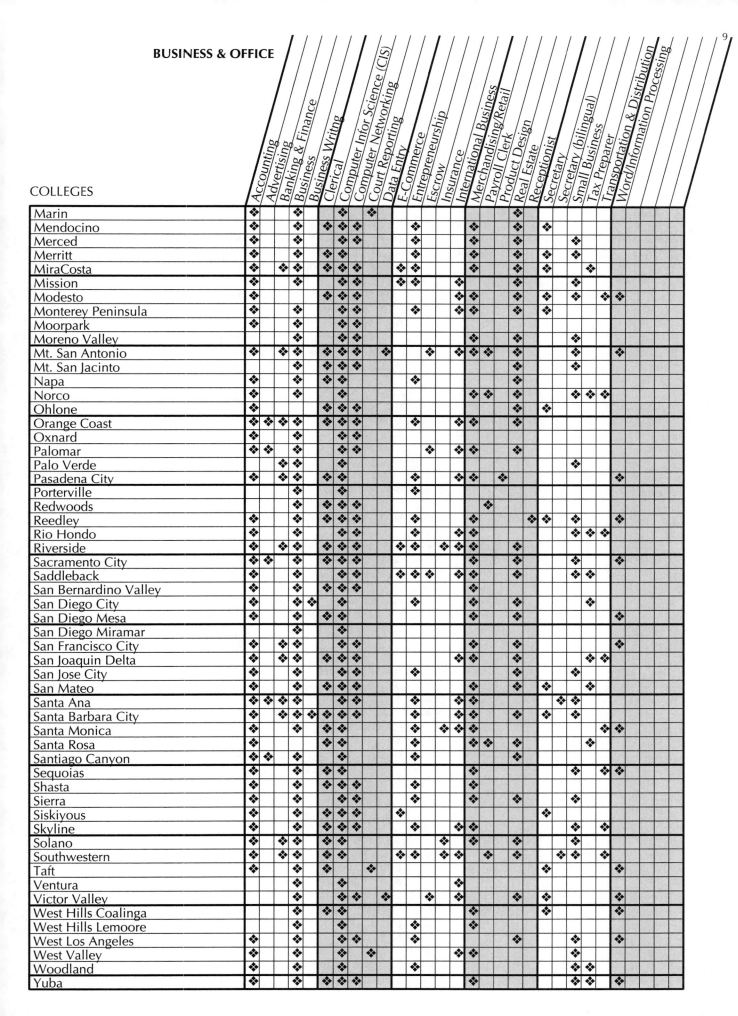

COLLEGES	Accounting	Advertising	Banking & Finance	Business	Business Writng	Clerical	Computer Infor Science (CIS)	Computer Networking	Court Reporting	Data Entry	E-Commerce	Entrepreneurship	Escrow	Insurance	International Business	Merchandising/Retail	Payroll Clerk	Product Design	Real Estate	Receptionist	Secretary	Secretary (bilingual)	Small Business	Tax Preparer	Transportation & Distribution	Word/Information Processing
Marin	❖			❖			❖		❖										❖							
Mendocino	❖			❖		❖	❖	❖				❖				❖			❖		❖					
Merced	❖			❖			❖	❖				❖				❖			❖				❖			
Merritt	❖			❖		❖	❖					❖				❖			❖		❖		❖			
MiraCosta	❖		❖	❖		❖	❖	❖			❖	❖				❖			❖		❖			❖		
Mission	❖			❖			❖	❖			❖	❖			❖				❖				❖			
Modesto	❖					❖	❖	❖							❖	❖			❖		❖		❖		❖	❖
Monterey Peninsula	❖			❖			❖	❖				❖			❖	❖			❖		❖					
Moorpark	❖			❖			❖	❖																		
Moreno Valley				❖			❖	❖								❖			❖				❖			
Mt. San Antonio	❖		❖	❖		❖	❖	❖		❖			❖		❖	❖	❖		❖				❖			❖
Mt. San Jacinto				❖		❖	❖	❖											❖				❖			
Napa	❖			❖		❖	❖					❖							❖							
Norco	❖			❖			❖									❖	❖		❖				❖	❖	❖	
Ohlone	❖					❖	❖	❖											❖		❖					
Orange Coast	❖	❖	❖	❖		❖	❖	❖				❖			❖	❖			❖							
Oxnard	❖			❖			❖	❖																		
Palomar	❖	❖		❖			❖	❖					❖		❖	❖			❖							
Palo Verde			❖	❖			❖																❖			
Pasadena City	❖		❖	❖		❖	❖					❖			❖	❖		❖								❖
Porterville				❖			❖					❖														
Redwoods				❖		❖	❖	❖									❖									
Reedley	❖			❖		❖	❖	❖				❖				❖				❖	❖		❖			❖
Rio Hondo	❖			❖			❖	❖				❖			❖	❖							❖	❖	❖	
Riverside	❖		❖	❖		❖	❖	❖			❖	❖		❖	❖	❖			❖							
Sacramento City	❖	❖		❖		❖	❖	❖								❖			❖				❖			❖
Saddleback	❖			❖			❖	❖			❖	❖	❖		❖	❖			❖				❖	❖		
San Bernardino Valley	❖			❖		❖	❖	❖								❖										
San Diego City	❖			❖	❖		❖					❖				❖			❖					❖		
San Diego Mesa	❖			❖		❖	❖									❖			❖							❖
San Diego Miramar				❖			❖																			
San Francisco City	❖		❖	❖			❖	❖								❖			❖							❖
San Joaquin Delta	❖		❖	❖		❖	❖	❖							❖	❖			❖					❖	❖	
San Jose City	❖			❖			❖	❖				❖							❖				❖			
San Mateo	❖			❖		❖	❖	❖								❖			❖		❖			❖		
Santa Ana	❖	❖	❖	❖			❖	❖				❖			❖	❖						❖	❖			
Santa Barbara City	❖		❖	❖	❖	❖	❖	❖				❖			❖	❖			❖		❖		❖			
Santa Monica	❖			❖		❖	❖					❖		❖	❖	❖									❖	❖
Santa Rosa	❖					❖	❖					❖				❖	❖		❖					❖		
Santiago Canyon	❖	❖		❖			❖					❖							❖							
Sequoias	❖			❖		❖	❖									❖							❖		❖	❖
Shasta	❖			❖		❖	❖	❖				❖				❖										
Sierra	❖			❖			❖	❖				❖				❖			❖				❖			
Siskiyous	❖			❖		❖	❖	❖			❖										❖					
Skyline	❖			❖		❖	❖	❖				❖			❖	❖							❖		❖	
Solano	❖		❖	❖		❖	❖							❖		❖			❖				❖			
Southwestern	❖		❖	❖		❖	❖				❖	❖		❖	❖		❖		❖			❖	❖		❖	
Taft	❖			❖		❖			❖												❖					❖
Ventura				❖			❖								❖											
Victor Valley				❖			❖	❖		❖			❖		❖				❖		❖					❖
West Hills Coalinga				❖		❖	❖									❖					❖					❖
West Hills Lemoore				❖			❖					❖				❖										
West Los Angeles	❖			❖			❖	❖				❖							❖				❖			❖
West Valley	❖			❖			❖		❖						❖	❖							❖			
Woodland	❖			❖			❖					❖											❖	❖		
Yuba	❖			❖		❖	❖	❖								❖							❖	❖		❖

COMMUNICATIONS

COLLEGES	Advertising Design	Animation	Dance	Digital Media	Digital Publishing	Graphic Arts, Digital	Illustration	Journalism	Mass Communications	Multimedia	Music	Photography	Radio/TV Broadcasting	Sign Language Technology	Technical Writing	Theater Arts	Translation	Video and Movie Production	Web Technology
Alameda																			❖
Allan Hancock		❖	❖	❖		❖				❖		❖		❖		❖		❖	
American River		❖		❖		❖	❖	❖	❖		❖			❖		❖	❖		❖
Antelope Valley		❖		❖		❖				❖	❖	❖		❖				❖	❖
Bakersfield								❖		❖				❖		❖			❖
Barstow												❖							
Berkeley City		❖		❖	❖				❖	❖				❖			❖		❖
Butte						❖			❖	❖		❖	❖			❖		❖	
Cabrillo		❖		❖	❖	❖		❖		❖								❖	❖
Cañada		❖		❖		❖				❖									❖
Canyons		❖		❖		❖			❖	❖		❖	❖	❖				❖	❖
Cerritos		❖				❖		❖	❖		❖		❖				❖		❖
Cerro Coso				❖															❖
Chabot				❖		❖	❖	❖	❖		❖	❖	❖			❖			
Chaffey				❖		❖	❖	❖		❖		❖	❖					❖	❖
Citrus																❖			
Coastline		❖		❖						❖									❖
Columbia				❖		❖				❖									❖
Contra Costa				❖		❖		❖											
Copper Mountain				❖		❖			❖										❖
Cosumnes River				❖	❖	❖		❖	❖	❖		❖	❖			❖		❖	❖
Crafton Hills						❖			❖							❖			❖
Cuesta						❖		❖			❖								❖
Cuyamaca				❖		❖						❖							❖
Cypress	❖	❖	❖	❖	❖	❖	❖			❖	❖	❖				❖		❖	❖
De Anza		❖				❖		❖	❖			❖	❖					❖	❖
Desert				❖	❖														
Diablo Valley		❖		❖		❖				❖	❖		❖					❖	❖
East Los Angeles		❖		❖	❖	❖		❖		❖	❖	❖				❖			
El Camino		❖	❖	❖		❖	❖	❖		❖	❖	❖		❖		❖		❖	❖
Evergreen Valley						❖			❖										
Feather River										❖									❖
Folsom Lake									❖										
Foothill				❖		❖	❖				❖	❖				❖		❖	❖
Fresno City			❖	❖		❖		❖		❖	❖	❖		❖		❖		❖	❖
Fullerton		❖		❖	❖	❖	❖	❖		❖	❖	❖	❖			❖		❖	❖
Gavilan				❖	❖	❖			❖	❖								❖	❖
Glendale		❖	❖	❖	❖	❖			❖	❖		❖	❖			❖		❖	❖
Golden West				❖		❖		❖						❖		❖		❖	❖
Grossmont			❖	❖				❖	❖	❖		❖		❖		❖		❖	❖
Hartnell				❖		❖						❖				❖			❖
Imperial Valley								❖		❖									❖
Irvine Valley		❖	❖	❖		❖						❖				❖			❖
Lake Tahoe											❖								
Laney				❖		❖				❖		❖	❖					❖	
Las Positas				❖				❖	❖		❖	❖							❖
Lassen				❖		❖													
Long Beach City			❖	❖	❖	❖		❖	❖			❖	❖			❖		❖	
Los Angeles City						❖		❖			❖	❖	❖			❖		❖	❖
Los Angeles Harbor																			
Los Angeles Mission		❖				❖			❖	❖								❖	❖
Los Angeles Pierce					❖	❖		❖			❖	❖		❖		❖			❖
Los Angeles Southwest								❖								❖			❖
Los Angeles Trade-Technical						❖													
Los Angeles Valley				❖		❖		❖		❖	❖	❖	❖			❖		❖	❖
Los Medanos						❖		❖			❖							❖	❖

COMMUNICATIONS

COLLEGES	Advertising Design	Animation	Dance	Digital Media	Digital Publishing	Graphic Arts, Digital	Illustration	Journalism	Mass Communications	Multimedia	Music	Photography	Radio/TV Broadcasting	Sign Language Technology	Technical Writing	Theater Arts	Translation	Video and Movie Production	Web Technology
Marin																			
Mendocino			❖													❖	❖		❖
Merced								❖	❖		❖	❖							
Merritt								❖											❖
MiraCosta		❖	❖	❖	❖	❖			❖	❖	❖	❖				❖		❖	❖
Mission				❖		❖	❖		❖	❖	❖						❖	❖	❖
Modesto				❖		❖						❖				❖			
Monterey Peninsula						❖						❖				❖			
Moorpark			❖			❖		❖		❖	❖	❖	❖			❖		❖	
Moreno Valley									❖	❖	❖						❖		
Mt. San Antonio	❖	❖	❖	❖	❖	❖	❖		❖		❖	❖	❖	❖		❖		❖	❖
Mt. San Jacinto						❖				❖				❖		❖			
Napa				❖		❖					❖	❖							❖
Norco		❖			❖						❖								❖
Ohlone		❖		❖	❖	❖		❖		❖	❖	❖	❖			❖		❖	❖
Orange Coast	❖		❖	❖		❖	❖			❖	❖	❖						❖	❖
Oxnard			❖	❖						❖	❖		❖	❖				❖	
Palomar		❖	❖	❖	❖	❖	❖	❖	❖	❖		❖	❖	❖		❖	❖		❖
Palo Verde		❖				❖													❖
Pasadena City				❖		❖		❖	❖		❖	❖				❖			❖
Porterville																			
Redwoods				❖						❖									
Reedley		❖		❖		❖					❖						❖		❖
Rio Hondo		❖				❖			❖	❖		❖				❖			❖
Riverside		❖	❖		❖	❖	❖			❖	❖	❖	❖	❖				❖	❖
Sacramento City		❖				❖	❖	❖		❖	❖	❖				❖		❖	❖
Saddleback		❖		❖		❖	❖	❖		❖		❖	❖	❖		❖		❖	❖
San Bernardino Valley				❖		❖				❖			❖					❖	❖
San Diego City				❖		❖	❖			❖	❖	❖	❖					❖	
San Diego Mesa		❖		❖	❖			❖		❖				❖					
San Diego Miramar									❖										
San Francisco City		❖		❖		❖		❖		❖		❖	❖				❖	❖	❖
San Joaquin Delta						❖			❖	❖		❖	❖	❖		❖			❖
San Jose City				❖				❖	❖	❖						❖		❖	❖
San Mateo				❖		❖		❖			❖	❖						❖	❖
Santa Ana		❖		❖	❖	❖		❖	❖	❖	❖	❖	❖	❖		❖		❖	❖
Santa Barbara City		❖	❖			❖		❖		❖		❖	❖		❖			❖	❖
Santa Monica		❖		❖	❖	❖		❖		❖		❖	❖			❖		❖	❖
Santa Rosa		❖		❖		❖	❖	❖		❖		❖						❖	❖
Santiago Canyon						❖				❖								❖	❖
Sequoias	❖					❖			❖								❖		
Shasta																			❖
Sierra				❖		❖	❖		❖	❖		❖		❖		❖			❖
Siskiyous						❖													❖
Skyline			❖					❖	❖	❖									
Solano						❖	❖	❖	❖			❖				❖		❖	❖
Southwestern				❖		❖		❖		❖	❖	❖	❖			❖	❖	❖	❖
Taft																			
Ventura								❖		❖		❖		❖		❖			
Victor Valley		❖		❖		❖		❖		❖		❖							❖
West Hills Coalinga													❖			❖			
West Hills Lemoore																			
West Los Angeles										❖			❖	❖		❖		❖	❖
West Valley			❖	❖	❖	❖										❖	❖	❖	❖
Woodland				❖						❖									
Yuba						❖			❖	❖		❖							❖

CRIMINAL JUSTICE

COLLEGES	Administration of Justice	Conservation Law Enforcement	Corrections	Court Management	Fingerprinting	Forensic Science	Police Academy	Probation & Parole	Security	Special Investigator
Alameda										
Allan Hancock	❖						❖			
American River	❖						❖			
Antelope Valley	❖									
Bakersfield	❖		❖							
Barstow	❖		❖							
Berkeley City										
Butte	❖			❖			❖			
Cabrillo	❖		❖							
Cañada										
Canyons	❖									
Cerritos	❖									
Cerro Coso	❖									
Chabot	❖									
Chaffey	❖		❖							
Citrus	❖									
Coastline										
Columbia										
Contra Costa	❖		❖			❖	❖		❖	❖
Copper Mountain	❖									
Cosumnes River										
Crafton Hills										
Cuesta	❖									
Cuyamaca										
Cypress									❖	
De Anza	❖		❖						❖	
Desert	❖	❖								
Diablo Valley	❖		❖					❖		❖
East Los Angeles	❖					❖	❖			❖
El Camino	❖					❖				
Evergreen Valley	❖						❖			
Feather River	❖									
Folsom Lake	❖									
Foothill										
Fresno City	❖		❖			❖	❖	❖		
Fullerton	❖						❖			❖
Gavilan	❖		❖							
Glendale	❖									
Golden West	❖						❖			❖
Grossmont	❖		❖	❖		❖			❖	
Hartnell	❖									
Imperial Valley	❖		❖	❖						
Irvine Valley	❖									
Lake Tahoe	❖									
Laney										
Las Positas	❖									
Lassen	❖						❖			
Long Beach City	❖									
Los Angeles City	❖				❖	❖				❖
Los Angeles Harbor	❖									
Los Angeles Mission	❖		❖				❖	❖		
Los Angeles Pierce	❖									
Los Angeles Southwest	❖				❖					
Los Angeles Trade-Technical	❖		❖							
Los Angeles Valley	❖		❖						❖	
Los Medanos	❖						❖			❖

CRIMINAL JUSTICE

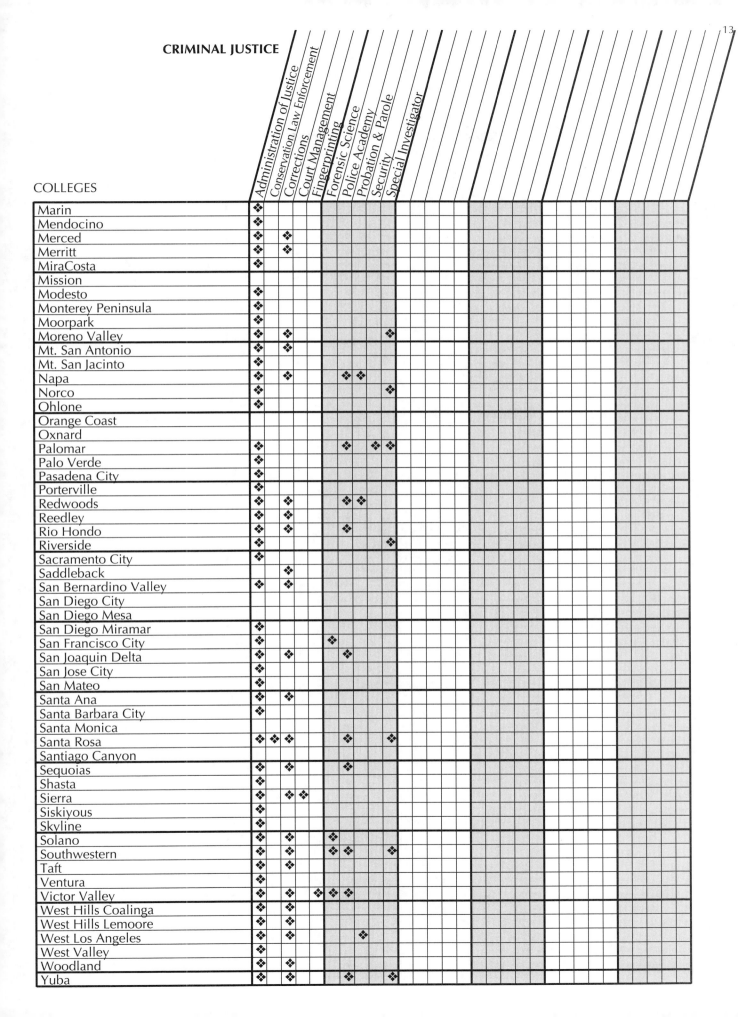

COLLEGES	Administration of Justice	Conservation Law Enforcement	Corrections	Court Management	Fingerprinting	Forensic Science	Police Academy	Probation & Parole	Security	Special Investigator
Marin	❖									
Mendocino	❖									
Merced	❖		❖							
Merritt	❖		❖							
MiraCosta	❖									
Mission										
Modesto	❖									
Monterey Peninsula	❖									
Moorpark	❖									
Moreno Valley	❖		❖							❖
Mt. San Antonio	❖		❖							
Mt. San Jacinto	❖									
Napa	❖		❖				❖	❖		
Norco	❖									❖
Ohlone	❖									
Orange Coast										
Oxnard										
Palomar	❖						❖		❖	❖
Palo Verde	❖									
Pasadena City	❖									
Porterville	❖									
Redwoods	❖		❖				❖	❖		
Reedley	❖		❖							
Rio Hondo	❖		❖				❖			
Riverside	❖									❖
Sacramento City	❖									
Saddleback			❖							
San Bernardino Valley	❖		❖							
San Diego City										
San Diego Mesa										
San Diego Miramar	❖									
San Francisco City	❖					❖				
San Joaquin Delta	❖		❖				❖			
San Jose City	❖									
San Mateo	❖									
Santa Ana	❖		❖							
Santa Barbara City	❖									
Santa Monica										
Santa Rosa	❖	❖	❖				❖			❖
Santiago Canyon										
Sequoias	❖		❖				❖			
Shasta	❖									
Sierra	❖		❖	❖						
Siskiyous	❖									
Skyline	❖									
Solano	❖		❖			❖				
Southwestern	❖		❖			❖	❖			❖
Taft	❖		❖							
Ventura	❖									
Victor Valley	❖		❖		❖	❖	❖			
West Hills Coalinga	❖		❖							
West Hills Lemoore	❖		❖							
West Los Angeles	❖		❖					❖		
West Valley	❖									
Woodland	❖		❖							
Yuba	❖		❖				❖			❖

ELECTRICAL-ELECTRONICS

COLLEGES	Audio Technology	Avionics, Aircraft Electronics	Cable Television	Computer Maintenance	Computer Security	Electrical Industrial	Electricity	Electro-Mechanics	Electronic Communications	Electronics Assembly	Electronics Service	Electronics Technology	Fiber Optics	Internet Technology	Laser Technology	Lighting Technology
Alameda																
Allan Hancock	❖							❖				❖				
American River	❖			❖	❖			❖	❖		❖	❖	❖			
Antelope Valley							❖					❖				
Bakersfield									❖			❖				
Barstow							❖									
Berkeley City																
Butte	❖															
Cabrillo				❖												
Cañada																
Canyons	❖															
Cerritos																
Cerro Coso																
Chabot												❖				
Chaffey			❖			❖	❖	❖					❖	❖		
Citrus	❖															
Coastline					❖							❖				
Columbia																
Contra Costa				❖	❖				❖				❖	❖		
Copper Mountain																
Cosumnes River				❖	❖									❖		
Crafton Hills																
Cuesta				❖		❖	❖	❖				❖		❖		
Cuyamaca				❖	❖			❖						❖		
Cypress				❖	❖											❖
De Anza					❖											
Desert																
Diablo Valley							❖					❖				
East Los Angeles												❖		❖		
El Camino				❖								❖				❖
Evergreen Valley																
Feather River																
Folsom Lake																
Foothill														❖		
Fresno City				❖	❖	❖	❖	❖	❖					❖		
Fullerton									❖					❖		❖
Gavilan				❖										❖		
Glendale				❖				❖				❖				
Golden West	❖															
Grossmont	❖															
Hartnell																
Imperial Valley						❖	❖					❖				
Irvine Valley						❖	❖					❖			❖	
Lake Tahoe																
Laney							❖		❖							
Las Positas					❖									❖		
Lassen																
Long Beach City							❖									
Los Angeles City				❖								❖		❖		
Los Angeles Harbor												❖				
Los Angeles Mission																
Los Angeles Pierce				❖			❖		❖			❖		❖		
Los Angeles Southwest				❖					❖			❖		❖		
Los Angeles Trade-Technical						❖	❖		❖			❖				
Los Angeles Valley				❖								❖				
Los Medanos				❖	❖		❖					❖				

ELECTRICAL-ELECTRONICS

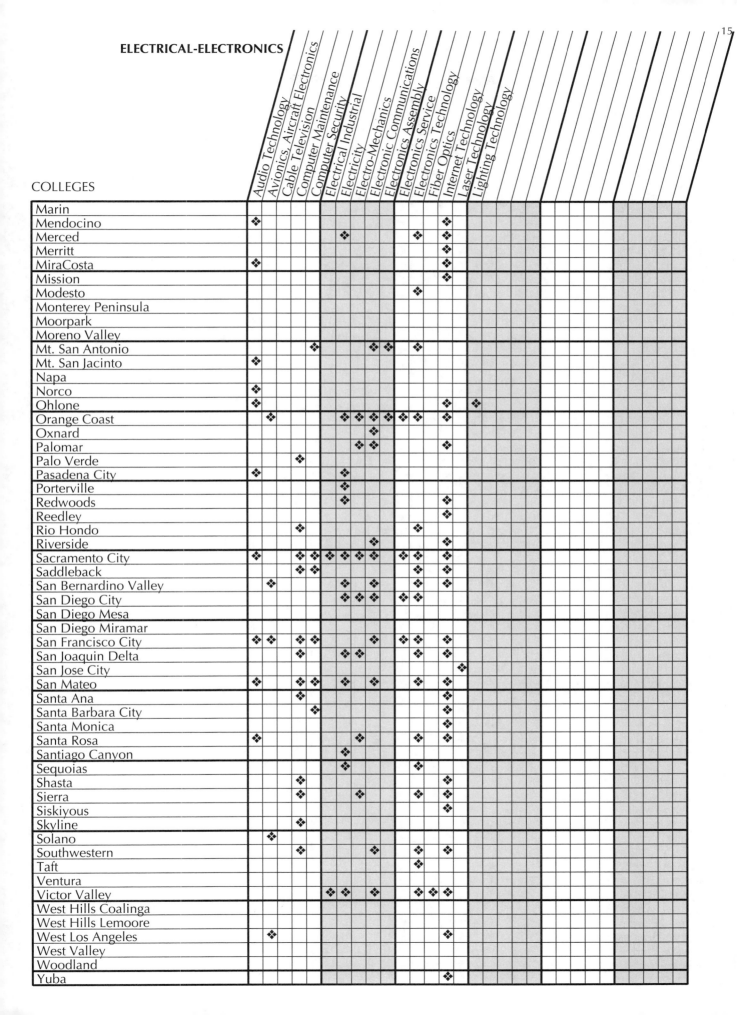

COLLEGES	Audio Technology	Avionics, Aircraft Electronics	Cable Television	Computer Maintenance	Computer Security	Electrical Industrial	Electricity	Electro-Mechanics	Electronic Communications	Electronics Assembly	Electronics Service	Electronics Technology	Fiber Optics	Internet Technology	Laser Technology	Lighting Technology
Marin																
Mendocino	❖													❖		
Merced							❖					❖		❖		
Merritt														❖		
MiraCosta	❖													❖		
Mission														❖		
Modesto												❖				
Monterey Peninsula																
Moorpark																
Moreno Valley																
Mt. San Antonio					❖				❖	❖		❖				
Mt. San Jacinto	❖															
Napa																
Norco	❖															
Ohlone	❖													❖		❖
Orange Coast		❖					❖	❖	❖	❖	❖	❖		❖		
Oxnard									❖							
Palomar								❖	❖					❖		
Palo Verde				❖												
Pasadena City	❖						❖									
Porterville							❖									
Redwoods							❖							❖		
Reedley														❖		
Rio Hondo				❖								❖				
Riverside									❖					❖		
Sacramento City	❖			❖	❖	❖	❖	❖	❖		❖	❖		❖		
Saddleback				❖	❖							❖		❖		
San Bernardino Valley		❖					❖		❖			❖		❖		
San Diego City							❖	❖	❖		❖	❖				
San Diego Mesa																
San Diego Miramar																
San Francisco City	❖	❖		❖	❖				❖		❖	❖		❖		
San Joaquin Delta				❖			❖	❖				❖		❖		
San Jose City															❖	
San Mateo	❖			❖	❖		❖		❖			❖		❖		
Santa Ana				❖										❖		
Santa Barbara City					❖									❖		
Santa Monica														❖		
Santa Rosa	❖							❖				❖		❖		
Santiago Canyon							❖									
Sequoias							❖					❖				
Shasta				❖										❖		
Sierra				❖				❖				❖		❖		
Siskiyous														❖		
Skyline				❖												
Solano		❖														
Southwestern				❖					❖			❖		❖		
Taft												❖				
Ventura																
Victor Valley						❖	❖		❖			❖	❖	❖		
West Hills Coalinga																
West Hills Lemoore																
West Los Angeles		❖												❖		
West Valley																
Woodland																
Yuba														❖		

ENGINEERING & TECHNOLOGY

COLLEGES	Aeronautics Production & Planning	Architectural Technology	Computer Game Development	Computer Programming	Computer Science	Drafting (CAD)	Electronic Microscopy	Engineering Technology	Engineering Technology (civil)	Inspection (building)	Marine Diving Technology	Materials Evaluation	Mechanical Technology	Metallurgical Technology	Nuclear Technology	Surveying	Tool Design
Alameda					❖												
Allan Hancock					❖	❖		❖	❖								
American River				❖	❖	❖		❖									
Antelope Valley				❖	❖	❖		❖									
Bakersfield		❖			❖	❖		❖									
Barstow					❖												
Berkeley City				❖	❖												
Butte				❖	❖	❖			❖								
Cabrillo		❖		❖	❖	❖		❖	❖	❖							
Cañada					❖												
Canyons					❖	❖		❖		❖						❖	
Cerritos		❖		❖	❖			❖									
Cerro Coso					❖			❖									
Chabot		❖		❖	❖			❖									
Chaffey		❖				❖											
Citrus						❖											
Coastline										❖							
Columbia					❖												
Contra Costa				❖	❖			❖									
Copper Mountain				❖	❖												
Cosumnes River		❖		❖	❖	❖		❖		❖							
Crafton Hills				❖	❖												
Cuesta				❖	❖			❖									
Cuyamaca				❖	❖	❖			❖			❖				❖	
Cypress			❖	❖	❖	❖											
De Anza				❖	❖	❖											
Desert		❖			❖	❖				❖							
Diablo Valley		❖		❖	❖	❖		❖		❖		❖					
East Los Angeles		❖		❖	❖	❖	❖	❖									
El Camino		❖			❖	❖		❖									
Evergreen Valley						❖		❖								❖	
Feather River					❖												
Folsom Lake				❖	❖												
Foothill																	
Fresno City		❖				❖		❖		❖							
Fullerton		❖		❖	❖	❖		❖	❖	❖							
Gavilan				❖	❖												
Glendale		❖		❖	❖	❖		❖									
Golden West			❖	❖	❖	❖											
Grossmont				❖	❖												
Hartnell					❖	❖		❖									
Imperial Valley					❖												
Irvine Valley				❖	❖	❖		❖									
Lake Tahoe					❖												
Laney		❖		❖	❖					❖							
Las Positas				❖	❖			❖									
Lassen																	
Long Beach City		❖		❖	❖	❖	❖										❖
Los Angeles City		❖		❖	❖	❖											
Los Angeles Harbor		❖			❖												
Los Angeles Mission																	
Los Angeles Pierce		❖		❖	❖	❖		❖									
Los Angeles Southwest				❖	❖	❖											
Los Angeles Trade-Technical		❖		❖	❖												
Los Angeles Valley		❖		❖	❖			❖				❖					
Los Medanos				❖	❖			❖									

ENGINEERING & TECHNOLOGY

COLLEGES	Aeronautics Production & Planning	Architectural Technology	Computer Game Development	Computer Programming	Computer Science	Drafting (CAD)	Electronic Microscopy	Engineering Technology	Engineering Technology (civil)	Inspection (building)	Marine Diving Technology	Materials Evaluation	Mechanical Technology	Metallurgical Technology	Nuclear Technology	Surveying	Tool Design
Marin																	
Mendocino					❖												
Merced					❖	❖		❖									
Merritt		❖															
MiraCosta		❖		❖	❖	❖			❖								
Mission				❖	❖			❖									
Modesto				❖	❖												
Monterey Peninsula					❖			❖									
Moorpark				❖	❖				❖								
Moreno Valley			❖														
Mt. San Antonio		❖	❖	❖	❖	❖		❖		❖							
Mt. San Jacinto						❖		❖									
Napa					❖												
Norco		❖	❖	❖	❖	❖		❖	❖								
Ohlone			❖	❖	❖			❖									
Orange Coast		❖		❖	❖	❖											
Oxnard																	
Palomar	❖		❖	❖	❖	❖				❖							
Palo Verde				❖	❖												
Pasadena City		❖		❖	❖	❖		❖		❖							
Porterville				❖	❖												
Redwoods		❖				❖											
Reedley					❖											❖	
Rio Hondo		❖	❖		❖	❖		❖	❖							❖	
Riverside				❖	❖												
Sacramento City	❖	❖	❖	❖	❖	❖		❖					❖			❖	
Saddleback						❖		❖		❖							
San Bernardino Valley	❖	❖		❖	❖	❖		❖		❖							
San Diego City						❖		❖									
San Diego Mesa		❖	❖	❖	❖	❖		❖									
San Diego Miramar					❖												
San Francisco City		❖	❖	❖	❖	❖		❖									
San Joaquin Delta		❖		❖	❖	❖	❖	❖	❖				❖				
San Jose City				❖	❖												
San Mateo		❖		❖	❖	❖		❖		❖							
Santa Ana				❖	❖	❖		❖	❖								
Santa Barbara City				❖	❖	❖					❖						
Santa Monica		❖	❖	❖	❖	❖											
Santa Rosa		❖	❖	❖	❖				❖							❖	
Santiago Canyon				❖	❖					❖						❖	
Sequoias		❖		❖	❖	❖				❖							
Shasta																	
Sierra		❖		❖	❖	❖		❖	❖								
Siskiyous			❖	❖	❖												
Skyline																	
Solano				❖	❖	❖											
Southwestern		❖	❖	❖	❖	❖		❖	❖	❖							
Taft																	
Ventura					❖	❖		❖									
Victor Valley		❖		❖	❖	❖		❖		❖							
West Hills Coalinga																	
West Hills Lemoore																	
West Los Angeles		❖			❖												
West Valley		❖		❖	❖	❖		❖									
Woodland																	
Yuba		❖			❖												

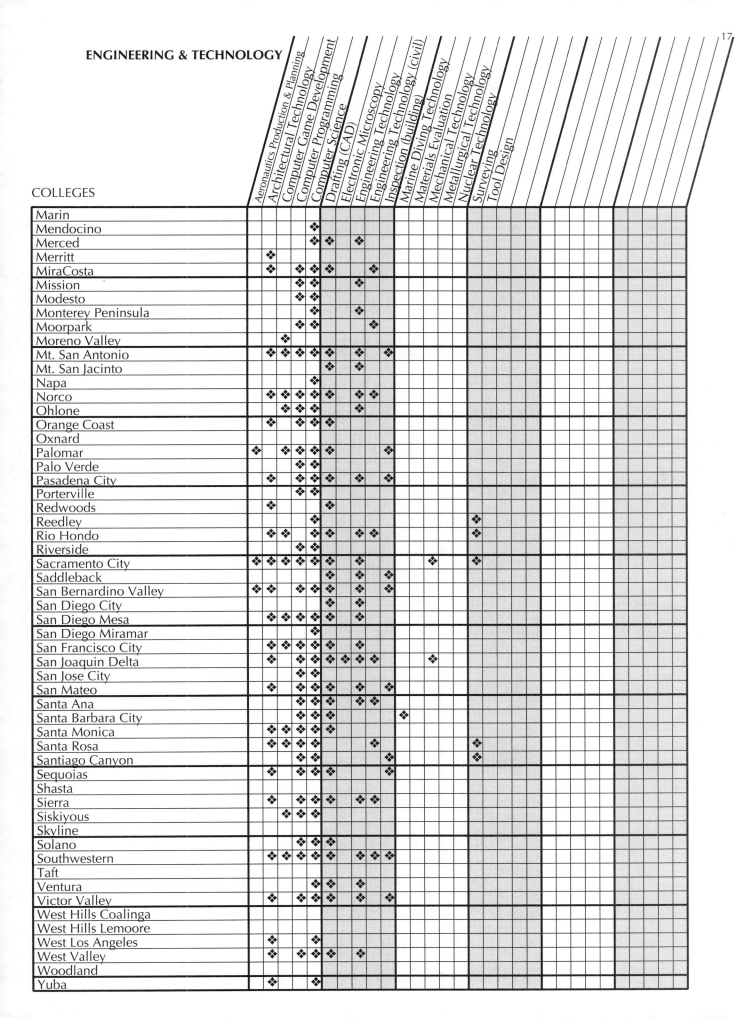

ENVIRONMENT & NATURAL RESOURCES

COLLEGES	Energy Technology	Environmental Technology	Forestry	Hazardous Materials	Land Fire Control	Natural Resources Management	Parks & Recreation Land	Solar Energy	Solid Waste Management	Sustainability	Urban Planning	Water Technology	Wildlife Management	Wind Energy
Alameda														
Allan Hancock		❖		❖	❖		❖							
American River	❖						❖	❖						
Antelope Valley					❖		❖							
Bakersfield			❖		❖									
Barstow														
Berkeley City														
Butte		❖				❖	❖			❖			❖	
Cabrillo	❖							❖		❖				
Cañada														
Canyons							❖	❖		❖		❖		
Cerritos														
Cerro Coso														
Chabot		❖												
Chaffey														
Citrus			❖									❖	❖	
Coastline														
Columbia			❖			❖						❖		
Contra Costa	❖													
Copper Mountain														
Cosumnes River	❖	❖								❖		❖		
Crafton Hills														
Cuesta														
Cuyamaca		❖										❖		
Cypress	❖													❖
De Anza	❖	❖											❖	
Desert		❖				❖	❖							
Diablo Valley	❖							❖						
East Los Angeles														
El Camino		❖					❖							
Evergreen Valley														
Feather River		❖	❖				❖					❖	❖	
Folsom Lake												❖		
Foothill		❖												
Fresno City														❖
Fullerton		❖												
Gavilan												❖		
Glendale														
Golden West	❖	❖						❖						
Grossmont														
Hartnell														
Imperial Valley	❖							❖				❖		
Irvine Valley								❖		❖				
Lake Tahoe		❖				❖				❖				
Laney		❖												
Las Positas														
Lassen														
Long Beach City	❖													
Los Angeles City														
Los Angeles Harbor														
Los Angeles Mission														
Los Angeles Pierce		❖				❖								
Los Angeles Southwest														
Los Angeles Trade-Technical	❖							❖	❖	❖	❖			
Los Angeles Valley								❖		❖				
Los Medanos														

ENVIRONMENT & NATURAL RESOURCES

COLLEGES	Energy Technology	Environmental Technology	Forestry	Hazardous Materials	Land Fire Control	Natural Resources Management	Parks & Recreation Land	Solar Energy	Solid Waste Management	Sustainability	Urban Planning	Water Technology	Wildlife Management	Wind Energy
Marin		❖												
Mendocino		❖												
Merced		❖												
Merritt		❖				❖	❖				❖			
MiraCosta														
Mission														
Modesto		❖	❖				❖							
Monterey Peninsula							❖							
Moorpark		❖												
Moreno														
Mt. San Antonio							❖					❖		
Mt. San Jacinto												❖		
Napa		❖												
Norco		❖												
Ohlone						❖								
Orange Coast		❖								❖				
Oxnard		❖												
Palomar												❖		
Palo Verde				❖										
Pasadena City								❖						
Porterville					❖			❖						
Redwoods			❖			❖		❖						
Reedley		❖	❖		❖	❖	❖							
Rio Hondo	❖	❖											❖	
Riverside														
Sacramento City		❖												
Saddleback		❖				❖								
San Bernardino Valley												❖		
San Diego City														
San Diego Mesa														
San Diego Miramar														
San Francisco City		❖						❖		❖				
San Joaquin Delta	❖													
San Jose City														
San Mateo	❖													
Santa Ana	❖				❖					❖				
Santa Barbara City		❖				❖						❖		
Santa Monica	❖	❖						❖		❖				
Santa Rosa		❖				❖	❖	❖		❖		❖		
Santiago Canyon		❖										❖		
Sequoias		❖										❖		
Shasta		❖	❖		❖	❖						❖		
Sierra	❖	❖						❖		❖		❖		
Siskiyous	❖													
Skyline								❖						
Solano				❖	❖							❖		
Southwestern	❖	❖		❖						❖	❖			
Taft	❖													
Ventura		❖				❖						❖		
Victor Valley	❖	❖				❖								
West Hills Coalinga														
West Hills Lemoore														
West Los Angeles														
West Valley							❖							
Woodland		❖												
Yuba														

HEALTH SERVICES

COLLEGES	Cardiovascular Technology	Certified Nurse Assistant (CNA)	Dental Assisting	Dental Hygiene	Emergency Medical, Paramedic	Fitness Specialist/Kinesiology	Gerontology	Health Occupations	Home Health Aide	Medical Assisting	Medical Insurance	Medical Lab Technician	Medical Office	Medical Records, Codes, Billing	Medical Transcription	Nursing (RN)	Nursing (vocational)	Occupational Therapy	Orthopedics	Phlebotomy	Physical Therapy	Psychiatric, Psychological	Radiology	Respiratory Therapy	Sonography	Sports Medicine, Athletic Trainer	Surgical Technology			
Alameda			❖																											
Allan Hancock		❖	❖		❖	❖			❖	❖				❖		❖	❖				❖									
American River					❖	❖	❖	❖								❖	❖							❖						
Antelope Valley										❖			❖			❖	❖						❖	❖						
Bakersfield					❖	❖										❖	❖						❖							
Barstow																														
Berkeley City										❖																				
Butte					❖	❖			❖				❖			❖	❖							❖						
Cabrillo				❖	❖					❖				❖		❖				❖			❖							
Cañada						❖				❖			❖	❖									❖							
Canyons		❖			❖	❖	❖					❖	❖			❖										❖				
Cerritos			❖	❖		❖				❖						❖	❖				❖	❖				❖				
Cerro Coso								❖		❖			❖				❖													
Chabot				❖		❖		❖		❖						❖	❖									❖				
Chaffey		❖	❖				❖		❖				❖				❖						❖							
Citrus			❖		❖											❖	❖													
Coastline						❖	❖	❖					❖	❖																
Columbia					❖								❖																	
Contra Costa						❖		❖		❖			❖		❖	❖														
Copper Mountain		❖			❖				❖							❖	❖													
Cosumnes River								❖	❖	❖	❖		❖	❖											❖					
Crafton Hills					❖			❖															❖	❖						
Cuesta					❖	❖				❖						❖	❖			❖		❖								
Cuyamaca																														
Cypress			❖	❖		❖		❖			❖		❖	❖	❖	❖						❖	❖		❖					
De Anza						❖		❖		❖	❖	❖	❖	❖	❖	❖				❖										
Desert		❖			❖	❖		❖	❖							❖	❖													
Diablo Valley			❖	❖		❖																		❖		❖				
East Los Angeles						❖	❖	❖		❖			❖	❖		❖	❖							❖						
ElCamino					❖	❖										❖	❖						❖	❖						
Evergreen Valley													❖			❖	❖													
Feather River						❖											❖									❖				
Folsom Lake							❖		❖			❖																		
Foothill			❖	❖	❖	❖							❖										❖		❖	❖				
Fresno City				❖	❖					❖			❖	❖		❖							❖	❖			❖			
Fullerton						❖						❖														❖				
Gavilan													❖			❖	❖													
Glendale					❖								❖	❖	❖	❖	❖													
Golden West						❖																								
Grossmont	❖					❖				❖			❖			❖		❖	❖					❖		❖				
Hartnell																❖	❖							❖						
Imperial Valley					❖					❖						❖	❖													
Irvine Valley						❖																								
Lake Tahoe			❖		❖					❖										❖	❖									
Laney																														
Las Positas																										❖				
Lassen						❖		❖									❖													
Los Beach City						❖				❖						❖	❖													
Los Angeles City		❖				❖		❖	❖				❖	❖	❖	❖							❖							
Los Angeles Harbor													❖			❖	❖													
Los Angeles Mission							❖	❖																						
Los Angeles Pierce																❖	❖													
Los Angeles Southwest						❖										❖														
Los Angeles Trade-Technical													❖			❖														
Los Angeles Valley																❖								❖						
Los Medanos					❖											❖	❖													

HEALTH SERVICES

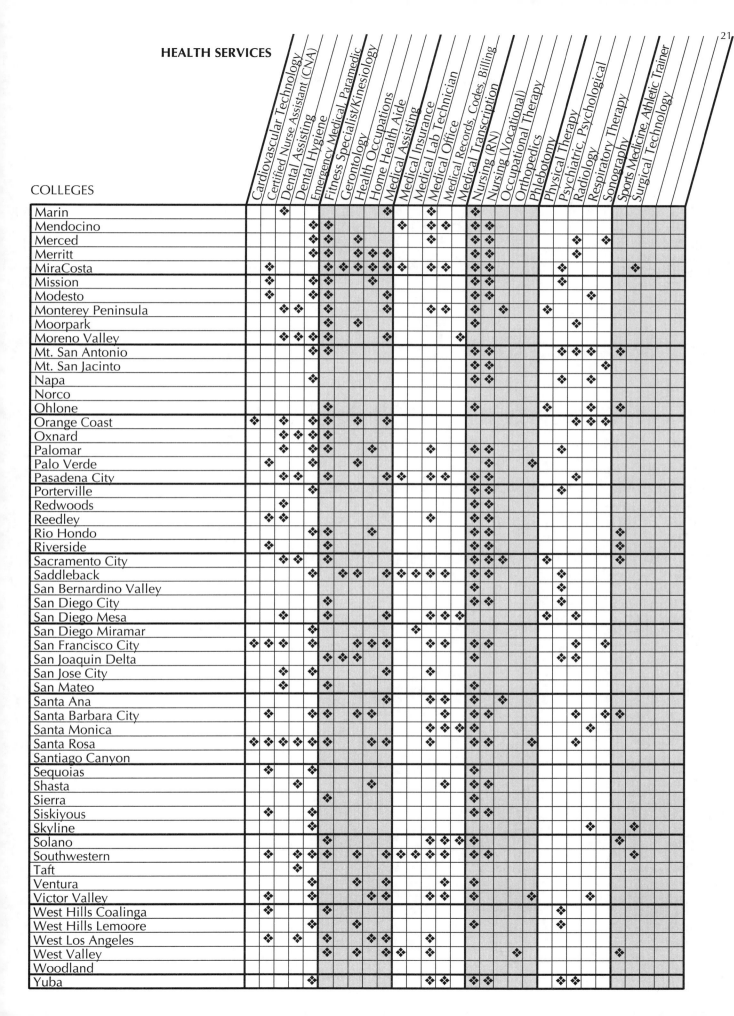

COLLEGES	Cardiovascular Technology	Certified Nurse Assistant (CNA)	Dental Assisting	Dental Hygiene	Emergency Medical, Paramedic	Fitness Specialist/Kinesiology	Gerontology	Health Occupations	Home Health Aide	Medical Assisting	Medical Insurance	Medical Lab Technician	Medical Office	Medical Records, Codes, Billing	Medical Transcription	Nursing (RN)	Nursing (Vocational)	Occupational Therapy	Orthopedics	Phlebotomy	Physical Therapy	Psychiatric, Psychological	Radiology	Respiratory Therapy	Sonography	Sports Medicine, Athletic Trainer	Surgical Technology
Marin			❖							❖			❖			❖											
Mendocino					❖	❖					❖		❖	❖		❖	❖										
Merced					❖	❖		❖					❖			❖	❖						❖		❖		
Merritt					❖	❖		❖	❖	❖						❖	❖						❖				
MiraCosta		❖				❖	❖	❖	❖	❖	❖		❖	❖		❖	❖					❖					❖
Mission		❖			❖	❖			❖							❖	❖					❖					
Modesto		❖			❖	❖				❖						❖	❖							❖			
Monterey Peninsula			❖	❖		❖				❖			❖	❖		❖		❖			❖						
Moorpark						❖		❖								❖							❖				
Moreno Valley			❖	❖	❖	❖				❖					❖												
Mt. San Antonio					❖	❖										❖	❖					❖	❖	❖		❖	
Mt. San Jacinto																❖	❖								❖		
Napa					❖											❖	❖					❖		❖			
Norco																											
Ohlone						❖										❖					❖			❖		❖	
Orange Coast	❖		❖		❖	❖		❖		❖													❖	❖	❖		
Oxnard			❖	❖	❖	❖																					
Palomar			❖		❖	❖			❖				❖			❖	❖					❖					
Palo Verde		❖			❖			❖									❖			❖							
Pasadena City			❖	❖		❖				❖	❖		❖	❖		❖	❖						❖				
Porterville					❖											❖	❖					❖					
Redwoods			❖													❖	❖										
Reedley		❖	❖										❖			❖	❖										
Rio Hondo					❖	❖			❖							❖	❖									❖	
Riverside		❖				❖										❖	❖									❖	
Sacramento City			❖	❖		❖										❖	❖	❖			❖					❖	
Saddleback					❖		❖	❖		❖	❖	❖	❖	❖		❖	❖					❖					
San Bernardino Valley																❖						❖					
San Diego City						❖										❖	❖					❖					
San Diego Mesa			❖			❖				❖			❖	❖	❖						❖		❖				
San Diego Miramar					❖							❖															
San Francisco City	❖	❖	❖		❖			❖	❖	❖			❖	❖		❖	❖						❖		❖		
San Joaquin Delta						❖	❖	❖								❖						❖	❖				
San Jose City			❖		❖					❖			❖														
San Mateo			❖			❖										❖											
Santa Ana										❖			❖	❖		❖		❖									
Santa Barbara City		❖			❖	❖		❖	❖					❖		❖	❖						❖		❖	❖	
Santa Monica													❖	❖	❖	❖								❖			
Santa Rosa	❖	❖	❖	❖	❖	❖			❖	❖			❖			❖	❖			❖			❖				
Santiago Canyon																											
Sequoias		❖			❖											❖											
Shasta				❖					❖					❖		❖	❖										
Sierra						❖										❖											
Siskiyous		❖			❖											❖	❖										
Skyline					❖																			❖			❖
Solano						❖							❖	❖	❖	❖										❖	
Southwestern		❖		❖	❖	❖		❖		❖	❖	❖	❖	❖		❖	❖										❖
Taft				❖																							
Ventura					❖			❖		❖				❖		❖											
Victor Valley		❖							❖	❖			❖	❖		❖				❖				❖			
West Hills Coalinga		❖				❖																❖					
West Hills Lemoore					❖			❖								❖						❖					
West Los Angeles		❖		❖		❖			❖	❖			❖														
West Valley						❖		❖		❖	❖		❖						❖							❖	
Woodland																											
Yuba					❖								❖	❖		❖	❖					❖	❖				

HOME ECONOMICS & FOOD SERVICE

COLLEGES	Baking	Catering	Child Nutrition	Clothing & Textiles	Costume Design & Construction	Culinary Arts	Dietary Technician	Dress Designing	Fashion Arts	Food Preparation	Food Service	Foods and Nutrition	Home Economics	Interior Design	Kitchen and Bath Design	Seamstress
Alameda								❖	❖							
Allan Hancock	❖	❖				❖	❖		❖	❖	❖			❖		
American River	❖				❖	❖		❖	❖					❖	❖	
Antelope Valley				❖				❖	❖			❖	❖	❖		
Bakersfield						❖	❖				❖	❖				
Barstow																
Berkeley City																
Butte							❖		❖					❖		❖
Cabrillo	❖	❖				❖				❖						
Cañada				❖	❖			❖	❖					❖	❖	❖
Canyons	❖					❖								❖		
Cerritos	❖					❖										
Cerro Coso																
Chabot													❖	❖	❖	
Chaffey					❖	❖	❖	❖	❖		❖	❖		❖		❖
Citrus																
Coastline																
Columbia						❖										
Contra Costa	❖					❖					❖	❖				
Copper Mountain						❖										
Cosumnes River						❖				❖	❖	❖				
Crafton Hills																
Cuesta												❖				
Cuyamaca																
Cypress	❖				❖	❖			❖	❖	❖					
De Anza																
Desert						❖										
Diablo Valley	❖					❖										
East Los Angeles																
El Camino					❖			❖	❖							
Evergreen Valley																
Feather River	❖	❖				❖										
Folsom Lake																
Foothill					❖											
Fresno City			❖			❖	❖				❖	❖	❖			
Fullerton				❖	❖			❖	❖			❖		❖	❖	❖
Gavilan																
Glendale						❖	❖					❖				
Golden West																
Grossmont	❖					❖				❖	❖					
Hartnell																
Imperial Valley																
Irvine Valley																
Lake Tahoe						❖										
Laney	❖					❖				❖						
Las Positas														❖		
Lassen																
Long Beach City	❖					❖	❖	❖	❖			❖	❖			
Los Angeles City					❖		❖							❖		
Los Angeles Harbor						❖										
Los Angeles Mission	❖					❖	❖			❖	❖	❖		❖		
Los Angeles Pierce					❖											
Los Angeles Southwest																
Los Angeles Trade-Technical	❖					❖		❖	❖							❖
Los Angeles Valley																
Los Medanos																

HOME ECONOMICS & FOOD SERVICE

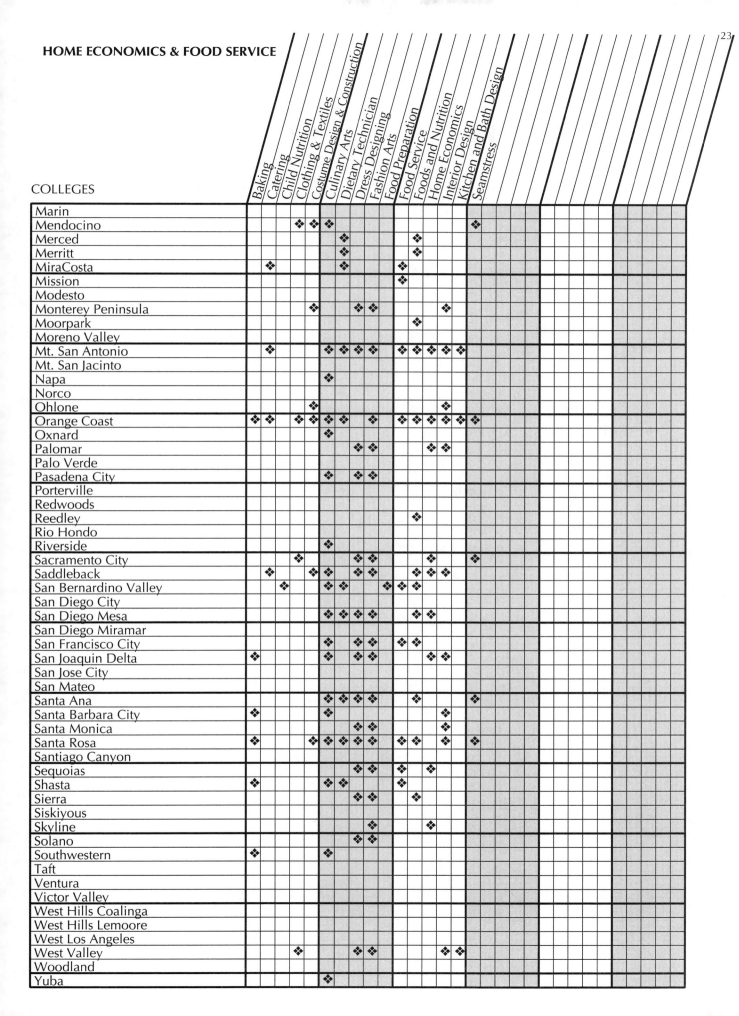

COLLEGES	Baking	Catering	Child Nutrition	Clothing & Textiles	Costume Design & Construction	Culinary Arts	Dietary Technician	Dress Designing	Fashion Arts	Food Preparation	Food Service	Foods and Nutrition	Home Economics	Interior Design	Kitchen and Bath Design	Seamstress
Marin																
Mendocino				❖	❖	❖										❖
Merced							❖					❖				
Merritt							❖					❖				
MiraCosta		❖					❖				❖					
Mission											❖					
Modesto																
Monterey Peninsula					❖			❖	❖					❖		
Moorpark												❖				
Moreno Valley																
Mt. San Antonio		❖				❖	❖	❖	❖		❖	❖	❖	❖	❖	
Mt. San Jacinto																
Napa						❖										
Norco																
Ohlone					❖									❖		
Orange Coast	❖	❖		❖	❖	❖	❖		❖		❖	❖	❖	❖	❖	❖
Oxnard						❖										
Palomar								❖	❖				❖	❖		
Palo Verde																
Pasadena City						❖		❖	❖							
Porterville																
Redwoods																
Reedley												❖				
Rio Hondo																
Riverside						❖										
Sacramento City				❖				❖	❖				❖			❖
Saddleback		❖			❖	❖		❖	❖			❖	❖	❖		
San Bernardino Valley			❖			❖	❖			❖	❖	❖				
San Diego City																
San Diego Mesa						❖	❖	❖	❖			❖	❖			
San Diego Miramar																
San Francisco City						❖		❖	❖		❖	❖				
San Joaquin Delta	❖					❖		❖	❖				❖	❖		
San Jose City																
San Mateo																
Santa Ana						❖	❖	❖	❖			❖				❖
Santa Barbara City	❖					❖								❖		
Santa Monica								❖	❖					❖		
Santa Rosa	❖				❖	❖	❖	❖	❖		❖	❖		❖		❖
Santiago Canyon																
Sequoias								❖	❖		❖		❖			
Shasta	❖					❖	❖				❖					
Sierra								❖	❖			❖				
Siskiyous																
Skyline									❖				❖			
Solano								❖	❖							
Southwestern	❖					❖										
Taft																
Ventura																
Victor Valley																
West Hills Coalinga																
West Hills Lemoore																
West Los Angeles																
West Valley				❖				❖	❖					❖	❖	
Woodland																
Yuba						❖										

MANAGEMENT & SUPERVISION

COLLEGES	Administrative Assistant	Aviation Management & Services	Business Administration	Construction Management	Customer Service	Economics	Food Service Management	Hotel-Motel Management	Human Resources Management	Industrial Management	Leadership, Business	Marketing	Office Administration	Project Management	Supervision	Supervision (government)
Alameda			❖										❖			
Allan Hancock	❖		❖		❖		❖					❖	❖		❖	
American River	❖		❖				❖				❖	❖				
Antelope Valley	❖		❖									❖	❖			
Bakersfield	❖		❖				❖									
Barstow	❖		❖													
Berkeley City	❖		❖										❖			
Butte			❖									❖				❖
Cabrillo			❖	❖				❖			❖			❖		
Cañada	❖		❖										❖			
Canyons	❖			❖	❖		❖	❖	❖			❖			❖	
Cerritos	❖		❖						❖			❖				
Cerro Coso			❖										❖		❖	
Chabot	❖		❖						❖			❖	❖	❖		
Chaffey	❖		❖				❖	❖				❖	❖	❖	❖	
Citrus													❖			
Coastline	❖		❖						❖		❖	❖	❖	❖	❖	
Columbia	❖		❖				❖	❖					❖			
Contra Costa			❖				❖									
Copper Mountain	❖		❖			❖										
Cosumnes River	❖		❖	❖			❖					❖	❖			
Crafton Hills			❖									❖				
Cuesta	❖		❖		❖					❖		❖	❖			
Cuyamaca	❖		❖										❖			
Cypress	❖	❖	❖		❖	❖	❖	❖				❖				
De Anza			❖									❖	❖	❖		
Desert	❖		❖	❖			❖		❖				❖			
Diablo Valley			❖	❖			❖				❖	❖			❖	
East Los Angeles	❖		❖		❖							❖	❖		❖	
El Camino			❖	❖								❖	❖			
Evergreen Valley			❖													
Feather River			❖									❖				
Folsom Lake	❖		❖									❖		❖	❖	
Foothill			❖												❖	
Fresno City	❖		❖				❖		❖			❖			❖	
Fullerton	❖		❖	❖	❖							❖		❖		
Gavilan						❖										
Glendale	❖	❖	❖				❖	❖				❖			❖	
Golden West	❖		❖						❖		❖	❖				
Grossmont	❖		❖					❖	❖			❖	❖		❖	
Hartnell			❖													
Imperial Valley	❖		❖	❖								❖		❖		
Irvine Valley	❖		❖												❖	
Lake Tahoe																
Laney			❖	❖			❖					❖			❖	
Las Positas	❖		❖									❖				
Lassen	❖												❖			
Long Beach City	❖		❖		❖							❖				
Los Angeles City	❖		❖									❖	❖		❖	
Los Angeles Harbor	❖		❖										❖			
Los Angeles Mission	❖		❖				❖	❖				❖				
Los Angeles Pierce	❖		❖									❖	❖		❖	
Los Angeles Southwest			❖			❖							❖		❖	
Los Angeles Trade-Technical	❖			❖			❖					❖			❖	
Los Angeles Valley	❖		❖									❖	❖		❖	
Los Medanos			❖												❖	

MANAGEMENT & SUPERVISION

COLLEGES	Administrative Assistant	Aviation Management & Service	Business Administration	Construction Management	Customer Service	Economics	Food Service Management	Hotel-Motel Management	Human Resources Management	Industrial Management	Leadership, Business	Marketing	Office Administration	Project Management	Supervision	Supervision (government)
Marin			❖										❖			
Mendocino	❖		❖										❖			
Merced			❖		❖								❖		❖	
Merritt	❖		❖		❖				❖				❖			
MiraCosta	❖		❖				❖	❖				❖	❖	❖	❖	
Mission	❖				❖		❖	❖	❖				❖			
Modesto												❖	❖		❖	
Monterey Peninsula			❖				❖	❖					❖			
Moorpark			❖													
Moreno Valley			❖									❖				
Mt. San Antonio	❖	❖	❖		❖		❖	❖	❖			❖				
Mt. San Jacinto			❖										❖		❖	
Napa			❖			❖		❖					❖		❖	
Norco			❖						❖			❖				
Ohlone	❖		❖										❖		❖	
Orange Coast	❖		❖	❖			❖	❖	❖		❖	❖	❖		❖	
Oxnard	❖		❖				❖									
Palomar	❖		❖									❖				❖
Palo Verde			❖													
Pasadena City	❖		❖					❖				❖				
Porterville			❖													
Redwoods							❖	❖								
Reedley	❖		❖		❖			❖								
Rio Hondo			❖									❖			❖	
Riverside	❖		❖						❖			❖	❖			
Sacramento City			❖		❖							❖	❖		❖	
Saddleback	❖		❖		❖						❖	❖				
San Bernardino Valley	❖	❖	❖				❖								❖	
San Diego City					❖						❖		❖		❖	
San Diego Mesa	❖		❖					❖				❖				
San Diego Miramar		❖	❖													
San Francisco City	❖				❖		❖	❖				❖			❖	
San Joaquin Delta	❖		❖									❖	❖		❖	
San Jose City			❖									❖				
San Mateo			❖						❖			❖		❖		
Santa Ana	❖		❖		❖			❖	❖			❖	❖		❖	
Santa Barbara City	❖		❖		❖			❖	❖			❖	❖			
Santa Monica	❖		❖									❖				
Santa Rosa	❖		❖		❖		❖	❖	❖			❖	❖	❖	❖	
Santiago Canyon			❖						❖			❖			❖	
Sequoias	❖						❖					❖				
Shasta	❖		❖		❖		❖	❖					❖			
Sierra	❖		❖		❖							❖			❖	
Siskiyous	❖		❖													
Skyline	❖		❖										❖		❖	
Solano	❖		❖							❖		❖				
Southwestern	❖		❖	❖			❖	❖			❖	❖	❖		❖	
Taft	❖		❖		❖											
Ventura	❖		❖			❖					❖				❖	
Victor Valley	❖		❖	❖			❖									
West Hills Coalinga			❖										❖		❖	
West Hills Lemoore			❖				❖	❖					❖			
West Los Angeles			❖					❖				❖				
West Valley			❖						❖		❖	❖		❖		
Woodland			❖						❖							
Yuba	❖		❖						❖				❖			

SCIENCE & LABORATORY

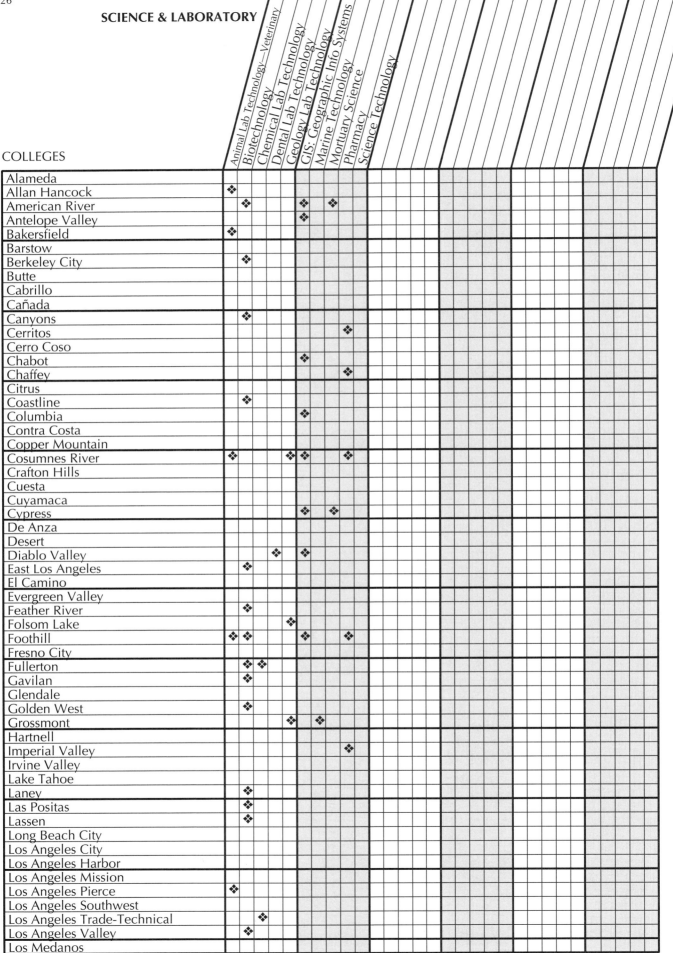

COLLEGES	Animal Lab Technology—Veterinary	Biotechnology	Chemical Lab Technology	Dental Lab Technology	Geology Lab Technology	GIS: Geographic Info Systems	Marine Technology	Mortuary Science	Pharmacy	Science Technology
Alameda										
Allan Hancock	❖									
American River		❖				❖		❖		
Antelope Valley						❖				
Bakersfield	❖									
Barstow										
Berkeley City		❖								
Butte										
Cabrillo										
Cañada										
Canyons		❖								
Cerritos									❖	
Cerro Coso										
Chabot						❖				
Chaffey									❖	
Citrus										
Coastline		❖								
Columbia						❖				
Contra Costa										
Copper Mountain										
Cosumnes River	❖				❖	❖			❖	
Crafton Hills										
Cuesta										
Cuyamaca										
Cypress						❖		❖		
De Anza										
Desert										
Diablo Valley				❖		❖				
East Los Angeles		❖								
El Camino										
Evergreen Valley										
Feather River		❖								
Folsom Lake					❖					
Foothill	❖	❖				❖			❖	
Fresno City										
Fullerton		❖	❖							
Gavilan		❖								
Glendale										
Golden West		❖								
Grossmont					❖		❖			
Hartnell										
Imperial Valley									❖	
Irvine Valley										
Lake Tahoe										
Laney		❖								
Las Positas		❖								
Lassen		❖								
Long Beach City										
Los Angeles City										
Los Angeles Harbor										
Los Angeles Mission										
Los Angeles Pierce	❖									
Los Angeles Southwest										
Los Angeles Trade-Technical			❖							
Los Angeles Valley		❖								
Los Medanos										

SCIENCE & LABORATORY

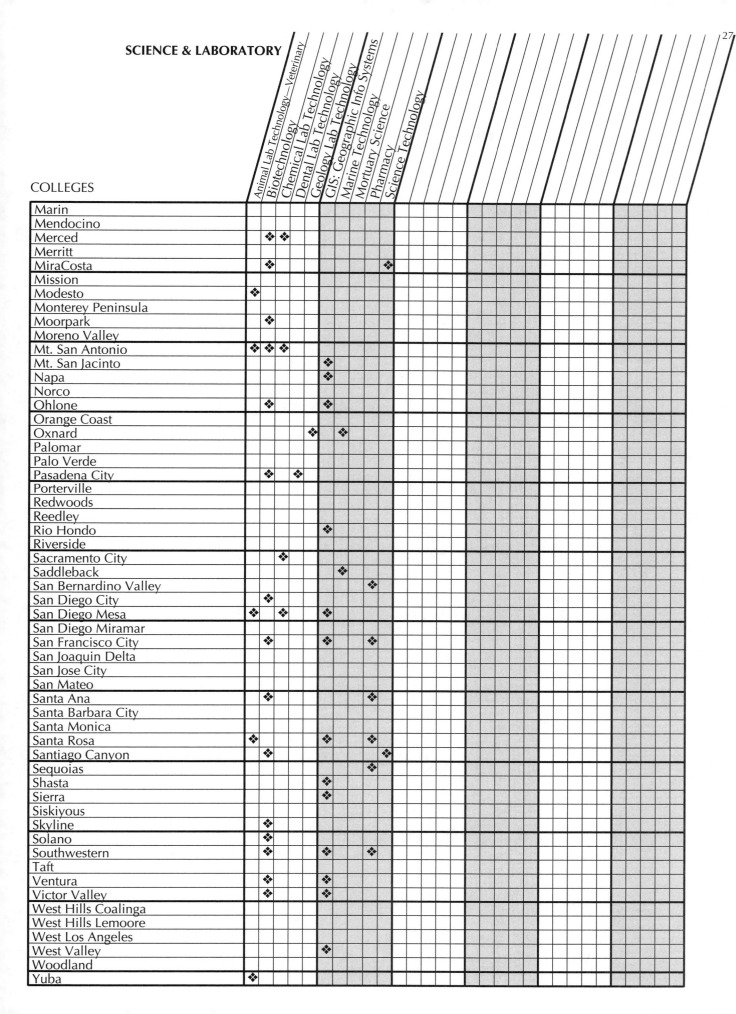

COLLEGES	Animal Lab Technology—Veterinary	Biotechnology	Chemical Lab Technology	Dental Lab Technology	Geology Lab Technology	GIS: Geographic Info Systems	Marine Technology	Mortuary Science	Pharmacy	Science Technology
Marin										
Mendocino										
Merced		❖	❖							
Merritt										
MiraCosta		❖								❖
Mission										
Modesto	❖									
Monterey Peninsula										
Moorpark		❖								
Moreno Valley										
Mt. San Antonio	❖	❖	❖							
Mt. San Jacinto						❖				
Napa						❖				
Norco										
Ohlone		❖				❖				
Orange Coast										
Oxnard					❖		❖			
Palomar										
Palo Verde										
Pasadena City		❖		❖						
Porterville										
Redwoods										
Reedley										
Rio Hondo						❖				
Riverside										
Sacramento City			❖							
Saddleback							❖			
San Bernardino Valley									❖	
San Diego City		❖								
San Diego Mesa	❖		❖			❖				
San Diego Miramar										
San Francisco City		❖				❖			❖	
San Joaquin Delta										
San Jose City										
San Mateo										
Santa Ana		❖							❖	
Santa Barbara City										
Santa Monica										
Santa Rosa	❖					❖			❖	
Santiago Canyon		❖								❖
Sequoias									❖	
Shasta						❖				
Sierra						❖				
Siskiyous										
Skyline		❖								
Solano		❖								
Southwestern		❖				❖			❖	
Taft										
Ventura		❖				❖				
Victor Valley		❖				❖				
West Hills Coalinga										
West Hills Lemoore										
West Los Angeles										
West Valley						❖				
Woodland										
Yuba	❖									

SERVICE

COLLEGES	Alcohol & Drug Studies	Coaching	Community Health	Cosmetology	Diversity, Child Development	Early Childhood Education	Early Intervention	Event Planning	Family Day Care	Fire Science/Technology	Flight Attendant	Foster Care	Human Services	Industrial Relations	Instructional Aide	Instructional Aide (bilingual)	Library Technology	Manicuring	Massage	Paralegal	Pilot Training	Public Relations	Public Service	Recreation Leadership	Special Education	Speech-Language Pathology	Travel
Alameda																											
Allan Hancock	❖			❖		❖				❖			❖							❖					❖		
American River	❖				❖	❖	❖			❖			❖		❖					❖				❖			
Antelope Valley						❖				❖					❖												
Bakersfield						❖			❖	❖			❖		❖												
Barstow				❖		❖			❖	❖																	
Berkeley City			❖										❖										❖				
Butte				❖	❖	❖				❖								❖		❖							
Cabrillo	❖				❖	❖				❖			❖		❖	❖											
Cañada			❖			❖							❖		❖					❖			❖				
Canyons						❖				❖										❖					❖		
Cerritos				❖		❖									❖					❖				❖	❖	❖	
Cerro Coso						❖							❖		❖					❖							
Chabot		❖				❖	❖			❖			❖		❖												
Chaffey		❖	❖			❖				❖					❖					❖							
Citrus				❖		❖											❖						❖				
Coastline													❖							❖							
Columbia						❖				❖					❖												
Contra Costa	❖					❖							❖														
Copper Mountain						❖				❖					❖												
Cosumnes River	❖		❖			❖	❖		❖	❖			❖		❖												
Crafton Hills						❖				❖					❖												
Cuesta	❖	❖				❖							❖				❖			❖				❖			
Cuyamaca						❖	❖													❖							
Cypress	❖	❖						❖			❖		❖							❖	❖						❖
De Anza						❖	❖												❖	❖					❖		
Desert	❖					❖				❖					❖									❖			
Diablo Valley	❖	❖				❖									❖										❖		
East Los Angeles	❖		❖			❖	❖			❖					❖					❖							
El Camino				❖		❖	❖			❖										❖				❖	❖		
Evergreen Valley																				❖							
Feather River						❖									❖									❖			
Folsom Lake						❖	❖		❖	❖			❖		❖												
Foothill						❖	❖								❖										❖		
Fresno City	❖					❖	❖		❖	❖		❖	❖		❖		❖			❖				❖			
Fullerton		❖		❖		❖	❖		❖						❖					❖		❖					
Gavilan				❖		❖	❖		❖							❖											
Glendale	❖					❖	❖			❖	❖				❖					❖	❖						
Golden West				❖		❖														❖							
Grossmont						❖							❖		❖												
Hartnell	❖					❖																					
Imperial Valley	❖					❖	❖			❖					❖					❖							
Irvine Valley						❖	❖								❖					❖							
Lake Tahoe	❖					❖				❖																	
Laney				❖										❖													
Las Positas		❖				❖			❖	❖			❖		❖												
Lassen	❖					❖				❖			❖		❖												
Long Beach City	❖					❖				❖			❖				❖								❖		
Los Angeles City	❖					❖	❖						❖		❖					❖					❖		
Los Angeles Harbor						❖				❖										❖							
Los Angeles Mission						❖	❖		❖						❖	❖				❖					❖		
Los Angeles Pierce	❖					❖	❖								❖					❖							
Los Angeles Southwest	❖					❖	❖								❖	❖				❖					❖	❖	
Los Angeles Trade-Technical				❖		❖	❖							❖	❖								❖		❖		
Los Angeles Valley						❖	❖			❖					❖	❖									❖		
Los Medanos						❖	❖			❖															❖		❖

SERVICE

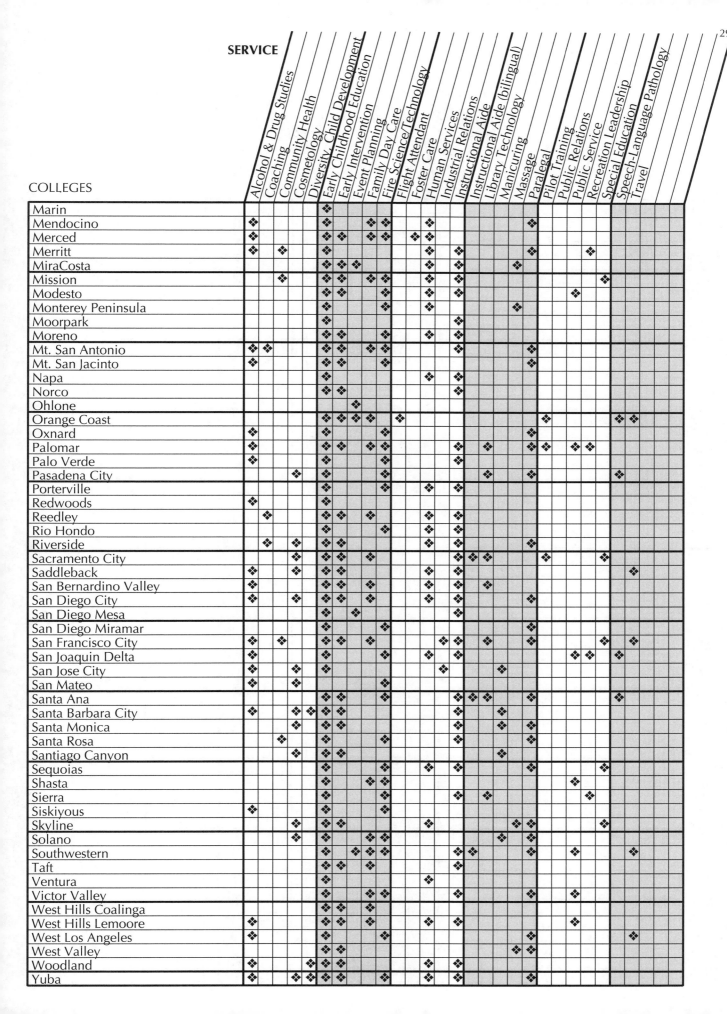

COLLEGES	Alcohol & Drug Studies	Coaching	Community Health	Cosmetology	Diversity, Child Development	Early Childhood Education	Early Intervention	Event Planning	Family Day Care	Fire Science/Technology	Flight Attendant	Foster Care	Human Services	Industrial Relations	Instructional Aide	Instructional Aide (bilingual)	Library Technology	Manicuring	Massage	Paralegal	Pilot Training	Public Relations	Public Service	Recreation Leadership	Special Education	Speech-Language Pathology	Travel
Marin						❖																					
Mendocino	❖					❖			❖	❖			❖							❖							
Merced	❖					❖	❖		❖	❖		❖	❖														
Merritt	❖		❖			❖							❖		❖					❖				❖			
MiraCosta						❖	❖	❖					❖		❖				❖								
Mission			❖			❖	❖		❖	❖			❖		❖										❖		
Modesto						❖	❖			❖			❖		❖								❖				
Monterey Peninsula						❖				❖			❖						❖								
Moorpark						❖									❖												
Moreno						❖	❖			❖			❖		❖												
Mt. San Antonio	❖	❖				❖	❖		❖	❖					❖					❖							
Mt. San Jacinto	❖					❖	❖			❖										❖							
Napa						❖							❖		❖												
Norco						❖	❖								❖												
Ohlone								❖																			
Orange Coast						❖	❖	❖	❖		❖										❖					❖	❖
Oxnard	❖					❖				❖										❖							
Palomar	❖					❖	❖		❖	❖					❖		❖			❖	❖		❖	❖			
Palo Verde	❖					❖				❖					❖												
Pasadena City				❖		❖				❖							❖			❖						❖	
Porterville						❖				❖			❖		❖												
Redwoods	❖					❖																					
Reedley		❖				❖	❖		❖				❖		❖												
Rio Hondo						❖				❖			❖		❖												
Riverside		❖		❖		❖	❖						❖		❖					❖							
Sacramento City				❖		❖	❖		❖						❖	❖	❖				❖				❖		
Saddleback	❖			❖		❖	❖						❖		❖												❖
San Bernardino Valley	❖					❖	❖		❖				❖		❖		❖										
San Diego City	❖			❖		❖	❖		❖				❖		❖					❖							
San Diego Mesa						❖		❖							❖												
San Diego Miramar						❖				❖										❖							
San Francisco City	❖		❖			❖	❖		❖					❖	❖		❖			❖					❖		❖
San Joaquin Delta	❖					❖				❖			❖		❖								❖	❖		❖	
San Jose City	❖			❖		❖								❖				❖									
San Mateo	❖			❖						❖																	
Santa Ana						❖	❖			❖					❖	❖	❖			❖						❖	
Santa Barbara City	❖			❖	❖	❖	❖								❖			❖									
Santa Monica				❖		❖	❖								❖			❖		❖							
Santa Rosa			❖			❖				❖					❖					❖							
Santiago Canyon				❖		❖	❖											❖									
Sequoias						❖				❖			❖		❖					❖					❖		
Shasta						❖			❖	❖													❖				
Sierra						❖				❖					❖		❖							❖			
Siskiyous	❖					❖				❖																	
Skyline				❖		❖	❖						❖						❖	❖					❖		
Solano				❖		❖			❖	❖								❖		❖							
Southwestern						❖		❖	❖	❖					❖	❖				❖			❖				❖
Taft						❖	❖		❖						❖												
Ventura						❖							❖														
Victor Valley						❖			❖	❖					❖					❖			❖				
West Hills Coalinga						❖	❖		❖																		
West Hills Lemoore	❖					❖	❖		❖				❖		❖								❖				
West Los Angeles	❖					❖				❖										❖							❖
West Valley						❖	❖												❖	❖							
Woodland	❖				❖	❖	❖						❖		❖												
Yuba	❖			❖	❖	❖	❖			❖			❖		❖					❖							

TRADE & INDUSTRY

COLLEGES	Air Conditioning & Refrigeration	Aircraft Maintenance	Apparel Production	Appliance Repair	Auto Body	Auto Machinist	Automated Electronic Controls	Auto Technology	Cabinet & Millwork	Carpentry	Construction Technology	Diesel Mechanic	Heating & Ventilation	Heavy Equipment Mechanic	Industrial Safety	Industrial Technology	Machine Tool	Maintenance Technology	Manufacturing	Marine Mechanics	Metal Technology	Motorcycle Repair	Numerical Control	Plumbing	Printing	Process Plant Operator	Sheet Metal	Smog Technician	Welding	Wood Technology
Alameda		❖			❖			❖				❖																		
Allan Hancock					❖			❖									❖		❖										❖	
American River					❖		❖	❖				❖																	❖	
Antelope Valley	❖	❖			❖			❖																	❖				❖	
Bakersfield								❖	❖		❖					❖			❖				❖						❖	❖
Barstow								❖				❖																	❖	
Berkeley City																														
Butte								❖						❖															❖	
Cabrillo											❖																		❖	
Cañada																														
Canyons						❖		❖			❖						❖		❖										❖	
Cerritos					❖			❖	❖							❖	❖						❖						❖	❖
Cerro Coso																❖	❖												❖	
Chabot								❖								❖	❖						❖						❖	
Chaffey		❖	❖					❖																				❖		
Citrus								❖																						
Coastline											❖															❖				
Columbia								❖																					❖	
Contra Costa					❖			❖					❖																	
Copper Mountain								❖																						
Cosumnes River							❖	❖			❖																	❖		
Crafton Hills																														
Cuesta					❖		❖	❖			❖																		❖	
Cuyamaca								❖																						
Cypress	❖				❖		❖	❖												❖		❖						❖		
De Anza						❖		❖											❖				❖					❖		
Desert	❖							❖			❖		❖															❖		
Diablo Valley	❖										❖		❖				❖	❖						❖	❖					
East Los Angeles								❖																	❖					
El Camino	❖				❖			❖	❖		❖		❖			❖	❖		❖				❖						❖	❖
Evergreen Valley								❖																				❖		
Feather River																														
Folsom Lake																														
Foothill																									❖					
Fresno City	❖				❖		❖	❖			❖		❖			❖		❖	❖								❖	❖	❖	
Fullerton								❖		❖	❖					❖	❖		❖				❖		❖			❖	❖	
Gavilan		❖																												
Glendale																	❖		❖				❖						❖	
Golden West								❖																				❖		
Grossmont																														
Hartnell								❖				❖				❖													❖	
Imperial Valley	❖				❖			❖		❖	❖																		❖	
Irvine Valley																❖			❖											
Lake Tahoe																														
Laney	❖						❖			❖			❖				❖	❖											❖	❖
Las Positas							❖	❖							❖														❖	
Lassen								❖									❖												❖	
Long Beach City																		❖									❖			
Los Angeles City																														
Los Angeles Harbor																														
Los Angeles Mission																														
Los Angeles Pierce								❖								❖							❖							
Los Angeles Southwest																														
Los Angeles Trade-Technical	❖				❖			❖	❖	❖	❖	❖				❖	❖	❖				❖	❖	❖		❖			❖	
Los Angeles Valley											❖					❖	❖		❖				❖							
Los Medanos	❖			❖				❖					❖													❖		❖	❖	

TRADE & INDUSTRY

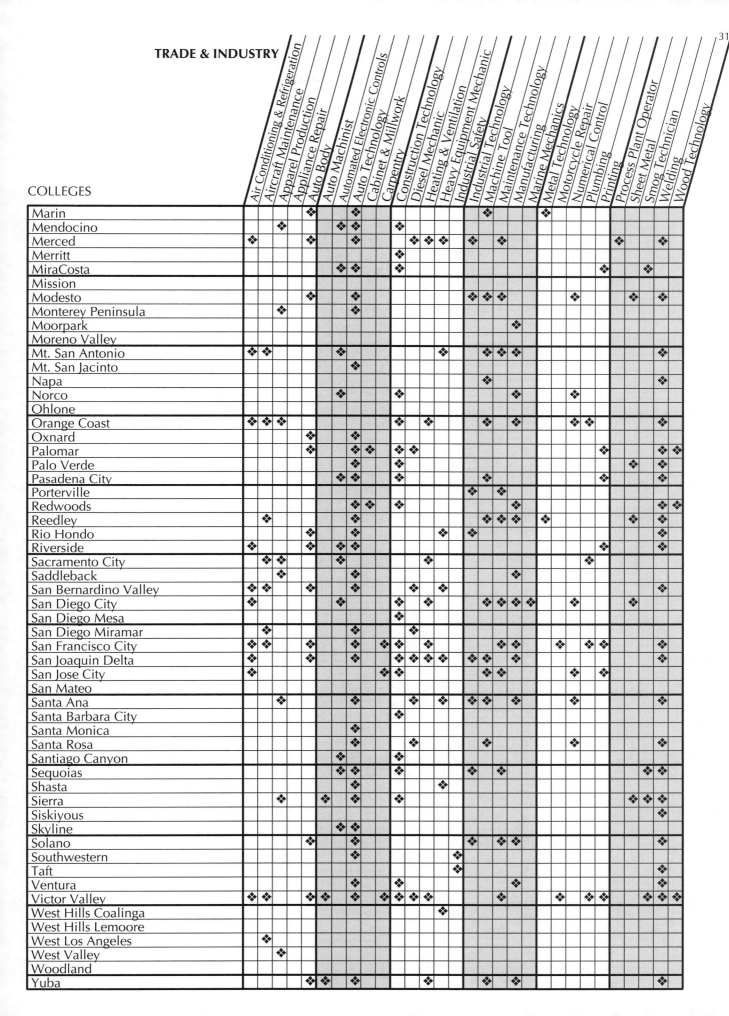

COLLEGES	Air Conditioning & Refrigeration	Aircraft Maintenance	Apparel Production	Appliance Repair	Auto Body	Auto Machinist	Automated Electronic Controls	Auto Technology	Cabinet & Millwork	Carpentry	Construction Technology	Diesel Mechanic	Heating & Ventilation	Heavy Equipment Mechanic	Industrial Safety	Industrial Technology	Machine Tool	Maintenance Technology	Manufacturing	Marine Mechanics	Metal Technology	Motorcycle Repair	Numerical Control	Plumbing	Printing	Process Plant Operator	Sheet Metal	Smog Technician	Welding	Wood Technology
Marin					❖			❖									❖				❖									
Mendocino			❖				❖	❖			❖																			
Merced	❖				❖			❖				❖	❖	❖		❖		❖								❖			❖	
Merritt											❖																			
MiraCosta							❖	❖			❖														❖			❖		
Mission																														
Modesto					❖			❖								❖	❖	❖					❖				❖		❖	
Monterey Peninsula			❖					❖																						
Moorpark																			❖											
Moreno Valley																														
Mt. San Antonio	❖	❖					❖							❖			❖	❖	❖										❖	
Mt. San Jacinto								❖																						
Napa																	❖												❖	
Norco							❖				❖								❖				❖							
Ohlone																														
Orange Coast	❖	❖	❖								❖		❖				❖		❖				❖	❖					❖	
Oxnard					❖			❖																						
Palomar					❖			❖	❖		❖	❖													❖				❖	❖
Palo Verde								❖			❖																❖		❖	
Pasadena City							❖	❖			❖						❖								❖				❖	
Porterville																❖		❖												
Redwoods								❖	❖		❖								❖										❖	❖
Reedley		❖						❖									❖	❖	❖		❖						❖		❖	
Rio Hondo					❖			❖						❖		❖													❖	
Riverside	❖				❖		❖	❖																	❖				❖	
Sacramento City		❖	❖				❖						❖											❖						
Saddleback			❖					❖											❖											
San Bernardino Valley	❖	❖			❖			❖				❖		❖															❖	
San Diego City	❖						❖				❖		❖				❖	❖	❖	❖			❖				❖			
San Diego Mesa											❖																			
San Diego Miramar		❖						❖				❖																		
San Francisco City	❖	❖			❖			❖		❖	❖		❖					❖	❖			❖		❖	❖				❖	
San Joaquin Delta	❖				❖			❖			❖	❖	❖	❖		❖	❖		❖										❖	
San Jose City	❖									❖	❖						❖	❖					❖		❖					
San Mateo																														
Santa Ana			❖					❖				❖		❖		❖	❖		❖				❖						❖	
Santa Barbara City											❖																			
Santa Monica								❖																						
Santa Rosa								❖				❖					❖						❖						❖	
Santiago Canyon							❖				❖																			
Sequoias							❖	❖			❖					❖		❖										❖	❖	
Shasta								❖						❖																
Sierra			❖			❖		❖			❖																❖	❖	❖	
Siskiyous																													❖	
Skyline							❖	❖																						
Solano					❖			❖								❖		❖	❖										❖	
Southwestern								❖							❖															
Taft															❖														❖	
Ventura								❖			❖								❖										❖	
Victor Valley	❖	❖			❖	❖		❖		❖	❖	❖	❖					❖				❖		❖	❖			❖	❖	❖
West Hills Coalinga														❖																
West Hills Lemoore																														
West Los Angeles		❖																												
West Valley			❖																											
Woodland																														
Yuba					❖	❖		❖					❖				❖		❖										❖	

SECTION 3
College Pages

Each college page lists location, size, calendar, housing, person in charge of occupational education, and other information. The list of occupational programs offered by the college indicates whether the program earns a certificate or an associate degree. The map at the end of this book shows college locations.

COLLEGE OF ALAMEDA

555 Ralph Appezzato Memorial Pkwy
Alameda CA 94501
510-522-7221
510-769-6019 Fax
alameda.peralta.edu

Semester system, 6 week summer session

Tim Karas, Vice President of Instruction

Enrollment: Full-time 6,079 Part-time 1,824

No Housing

OCCUPATIONAL PROGRAMS

Apparel Design and Merchandising	A	C
Auto Body and Paint		
Auto Body	A	C
Auto Paint	A	C
Automotive Technology		
Automotive Electronics Specialist	A	C
Chassis and Drivetrain	A	C
Chassis Specialist	A	C
Drivetrain Specialist	A	C
Engine Performance	A	C
Engine Repair Specialist	A	C
Green Diesel Technician		C
Light-Duty Auto Repair		C
Toyota Specialist		C
Aviation Maintenance Technology		
Airframe Technician	A	C
Powerplant Technician	A	C
Business		
Accounting	A	C
Business Administration	A	
Office Administration for the Logistics Industry		C
Small Business Administration		C
Computer Information Systems		
Business Information System		C
Computer Information Systems	A	C
Desktop Support Technician		C
Web Publishing		C
Dental Assisting	A	C
Diesel Mechanics	A	C

A—Associate Degree Program C—Certificate Program

ALLAN HANCOCK COLLEGE

800 South College Dr
Santa Maria CA 93454
805-922-6966
805-922-8722 Fax
www.hancockcollege.edu

Larissa Nazarenko, Dean of Academic Affairs

Enrollment: Full-time 4,676 Part-time 6,730

Semester System, 6 & 8 week summer sessions

No Housing

OCCUPATIONAL PROGRAMS

Program	Associate	Certificate
Accounting	A	
Administration of Justice	A	
Agri-Business		
Enology/Viticulture	A	
Pairing Wine and Food		C
Viticulture	A	C
Wine Marketing and Sales	A	C
American Sign Language	A	C
Applied Design/Media		
Animation	A	
Graphics	A	
Multimedia Arts and Communication	A	
Photography	A	
Website Design		C
Architectural Drafting	A	C
Auto Body Technology	A	
Auto Body Metal		C
Auto Body Refinishing		C
Automotive Technology		
Auto Engine Rebuilding	A	
Auto Service Management	A	
Auto Tune-Up & Diagnostic Procedures	A	
Automotive Chassis	A	
General Technician– Engine, Power Train Specialist		C
General Technician– Tune-up Emission Control Specialist		C
Business	A	C
Business Administration		C
Business Management		C
Business Marketing		C
Business Law		C
Customer Service		C
Executive Leadership		C
Human Resource Management		C
Sales and Marketing		C
Supervisory Management		C
Computer Business Information Systems	A	C
Computer Business Office Software		C
Database Administration		C
Information Architecture		C
Information Technology Fundamentals		C
MAC Fundamentals for Business		C
Office Software Support		C
Office System Analysis		C
Small Business Web Master		C
Computer Business Office Technology		
Administrative Assistant/Secretarial	A	C
Administrative Office Skills		C
Computer Business Office Skills		C
Computer Business Presentations and Publishing		C
Legal Secretarial	A	C
Word/Information Processing	A	C
Computer Science	A	
Cosmetology	A	C
Culinary Arts and Management		
Baking		C
Catering and Events Managements		C
Dietetic Service Supervision		C
Food Production Supervision		C
Food Service Production		C
Restaurant Management		C
Culinology®	A	
Dance	A	
Dental Assisting	A	C
Drama	A	
Early Childhood Education	A	C
Early Childhood Studies		
Elementary Education	A	C
Elementary Education—Bilingual/Bicultural Emphasis	A	C
General	A	C
Preschool/Infant Toddler Program	A	C
Special Education	A	C
Electronics Technology		
Digital Systems Technician		C
Electronic Engineering Technology	A	
Electronics Training		C
Mechatronics	A	C
Network Maintenance/Digital Technologies	A	C
Emergency Medical Services	A	C
Advanced Cardiac Life Support		C
Emergency Medical Services Academy		C
Emergency Medical Technician 1 (Basic)		C
EMT1 (Basic) Refresher		C
First Responder Update		C
Paramedic Training		C
Engineering	A	

A—Associate Degree Program C—Certificate Program

ALLAN HANCOCK COLLEGE (continued)

Engineering Technology		
Civil Engineering	A	
Engineering Drafting		C
Mechatronics	A	C
Entrepreneurship		
Entrepreneurship and Small Business Management	A	
Environmental Health and Safety	A	C
Environmental Health and Safety		C
Hazardous Materials General Site Worker		
Family & Consumer Sciences		
Fashion Studies	A	C
Fashion Merchandising		C
General	A	
Interior Design Merchandising	A	C
Film and Video Production	A	C
Fire Technology	A	C
Firefighter Academy		C
Human Services		
Addiction Studies	A	C
Co-occurring Disorders		C
Family Studies		C
Family Services Worker 1		C
Family Services Worker 2		C
Family Services Worker 3		C
General	A	C
Specialized Helping Approaches		C
Kinesiology	A	
Law Enforcement Training/Academy		
Basic Law Enforcement Academy	A	
Machine and Manufacturing Technology	A	
Medical Assisting		
Medical Assisting		C
Medical Billing and Coding		C
Nursing		
"30 Unit" Option		C
Certified Home Health Aide		C
Certified Nursing Assistant (CNA)		C
EKG/ Monitor Observer		C
Licensed Vocational Nursing (LVN)		C
Restorative Aide		C
Registered Nursing (RN)	A	C
Paralegal Studies	A	
Recreation Management	A	
Physical Education	A	
Sound Technology		C
Theatre		
Acting	A	
Design/Technical Theatre		C
Veterinarian Technician (RVT)	A	C
Welding Technology	A	C
Metal Fabrication		C
Pipe Welding		C
Wildland Fire Technology		
Logistics, Finance, Planning	A	C
Operations	A	C
Prevention, Investigation, Prescribed Burning	A	C

A—Associate Degree Program C—Certificate Program

AMERICAN RIVER COLLEGE ARC

4700 College Oak Dr
Sacramento CA 95841
916-484-8202
916-484-8209 Fax
www.arc.losrios.edu

Jerome Countee, Associate Vice President of Workforce Education

Enrollment: Full-time 14,028 Part-time 44,626

Semester System; 4, 6, & 8 Week Summer Sessions

No Housing

OCCUPATIONAL PROGRAMS

Accounting	A	C
Clerk		C
Taxation		C
Administration of Justice	A	
Art New Media	A	
3D Animation		C
Graphic Design		C
Illustration		C
Modeling and Texturing		C
Technical Communication	A	C
Web Design		C
Automotive Technology	A	C
Air Conditioning Service		C
Alternative Fuels		C
Analysis	A	C
Claims Estimator		C
Component Service Technician	A	C
Collision Technology	A	C
Extreme Tuner		C
Parts and Service		C
Service Technician		C
Transmission Service		C
Undercar Service		C
Biotechnology	A	C
Business General	A	C
Small Business Management	A	C
Business Technology		
Administrative Assistant	A	
Law Office Assistant		C
Office Technology		C
Virtual Office Professional		C
Computer Science	A	
CIS: Computer Networking Management	A	C
CIS: Computer Programming	A	C
CIS: Database Management	A	C
CIS: Microcomputer Applications	A	C
CIS: PC Support Management	A	
CIS: PC Support		C
Information Security Essentials		C
Information Systems Security	A	C
Network Administration Essentials—Windows		C
Technical Communications	A	C

Web Developer		C
Web Publishing		C
Design and Engineering Technology		
Design Technology	A	C
Engineering Technology		C
Diesel/Clean Diesel Technology		
Clean Diesel Technology		C
Diesel Technology	A	C
Preventive Maintenance		C
Early Childhood Education	A	
Associate Teacher		C
Culture and Diversity Specialist		C
Infant Specialist		C
Management Specialist		C
Master Teacher		C
School Age		C
Site Supervisor		C
Teacher		C
Electronics Technology		
Basic Advanced Electronics and Telecommunications		C
Biomedical Equipment Technology		C
Digital Home Technology Integrator		C
Digital Repair and Upgrade Technician		C
Electronic Systems Technology	A	C
Fiber Optics		C
Mechtronics	A	C
Robotics		C
Telecommunication Specialist		C
Energy		
Solar Energy Systems Design, Estimation, and Sales		C
Solar Energy Technology		C
Fashion Design	A	C
Fashion Merchandising	A	C
Fire Technology	A	C
Fitness Specialist		C
Funeral Service Education	A	
Geographic Information Systems (GIS)	A	
Geographic Information Systems and Interdisciplinary App		C
Gerontology	A	C

A—Associate Degree Program C—Certificate Program

AMERICAN RIVER COLLEGE (continued)

Healthcare Interpreting		C
Horticulture		
Design Technology	A	C
Floristry		C
Landscape Industry	A	C
Hospitality Management		
Culinary Arts/Restaurant Management	A	C
Introductory Baking		C
Restaurant Management	A	
Human Services	A	C
Chemical Dependency	A	C
Interior Design	A	
Interior Planning & Design	A	
Para Professional Interior Planning and Design		C
Journalism and Mass Communication	A	
Landscape Design Technology	A	C
Legal Assisting	A	C
Law Office Clerical Assistant		C
Management	A	C
Leadership		C
Marketing	A	
Advertising and Sales Promotion	A	
Retail Management	A	C
Music–Commercial Music		
Business	A	C
Recording	A	C
Nursing and Allied Health		
LVN		C
LVN to RN Career Mobility	A	
Registered Nursing	A	
Paramedic Program	A	C
POST Academy		
Basic Law Enforcement Academy—Module I		C
Basic Law Enforcement Academy—Module II		C
Basic Law Enforcement Academy—Module III		C
Real Estate	A	C
Recreation Management	A	
Respiratory Care	A	
Sign Language Studies		
Business	A	C
Human Services	A	C
Interpreter Training	A	C
Theatre Arts		
Acting	A	
Children Theatre		C
Costuming		C
Film		C
Technical	A	
Welding Technology	A	C
Gas Metal Arc and Flux Cored Arc Welding Plate		C
Gas Tungsten Arc Plate and Pipe Welding		C
Shielded Metal Arc Plate and Pipe Welding		C
Metallurgy and Inspection		C

A—Associate Degree Program C—Certificate Program

ANTELOPE VALLEY COLLEGE

3041 West Ave K
Lancaster CA 93536-5426
661-722-6300
661-722-6329 Fax
www.avc.edu

Dr. Karen Cowell, Dean of Career Technical Education

Enrollment: Full-time 4,594 Part-time 9,676

Semester system, 6, 8 & 12 week summer session

No Housing

OCCUPATIONAL PROGRAMS

Administration of Justice	A	
Aeronautical and Aviation Technology		
Aircraft Airframe	A	C
Aircraft Fabrication and Assembly	A	C
Aircraft Powerplant	A	C
General Aircraft Maintenance	A	C
Agriculture/Park and Landscape Management		
Environmental Horticulture	A	C
Landscaping Construction	A	C
Air Conditioning and Refrigeration		
Air Conditioning Specialist	A	C
Air Conditioning and Refrigeration Specialist	A	C
Refrigeration Specialist	A	C
Auto Body		
Collision Repair and Refinishing Specialist	A	C
Collision Repair Specialist	A	C
Refinishing Specialist	A	C
Automotive Technology		
Driveability, Emissions and Electrical	A	C
Engine and Drive Trains	A	C
Business		
Business Administration	A	
General Business	A	C
Professional Bookkeeping	A	C
Child and Family Education	A	C
School-Aged Child Care	A	C
Clothing and Textiles—Fashion Design	A	C
Computer Applications	A	C
Computer Networking Core		C
Computer Networking Multi-Platform	A	C
Computer Information Science		
Business Computer Information Science	A	C
Computer Software Developer	A	C
Deaf Studies		
American Sign Language	A	C
Interpreter Training	A	C
Digital Media	A	C
Computer Animation	A	C
Digital Photographic Imaging	A	C
Digital Printing	A	C
Graphic Design	A	C
Interactive Media—Web Design	A	C
Video Design and Production	A	C
Drafting/Computer Aided Design	A	C
Education–Instructional Aide	A	C
Electrical Technology	A	C
Electronics Technology	A	C
Engineering	A	
Engineering Technology	A	C
Family and Consumer Education		
Child and Family Development	A	
Clothing and Textiles	A	
Consumer Services	A	
Interior Design	A	
Nutrition and Foods	A	
Fire Technology	A	C
Firefighter I Academy		C
Wildland Fire Technology	A	
Geosciences		
Geographic Information System (GIS)		C
Management	A	C
Small Business	A	C
Marketing	A	C
Medical Assisting		
Clinical Medical Assistant	A	C
Medical Assistant	A	C
Music—Commercial		
Level I—General		C
Level II—Performance Specialty		C
Nursing Science		
Licensed Vocational Nurse		C
Registered Nursing	A	
Office Technology		
Administrative Assistant	A	C
Administrative Medical Assistant	A	C
Office Specialist	A	C
Photography—Commercial and Photographic Imaging		
Commercial Photography	A	C
Radiologic Technology	A	
Real Estate	A	
Real Estate Broker		C
Real Estate Salesperson		C

A—Associate Degree Program C—Certificate Program

ANTELOPE VALLEY COLLEGE (continued)

Respiratory Therapy	A	
Welding	A	C

A—Associate Degree Program C—Certificate Program

BAKERSFIELD COLLEGE

1801 Panorama Dr
Bakersfield CA 93305-1299
661-395-4011
661-395-4765 Fax
www.bakersfieldcollege.edu

Michele Bresso, Dean of Career and Technical Education

Enrollment: Full-time 6,147 Part-time 12,156

Semester system

No Housing

OCCUPATIONAL PROGRAMS

Agriculture		
Agriculture Business Management	A	C
Animal Science	A	C
Environmental Horticulture	A	C
Forestry	A	C
Plant Science	A	C
Registered Veterinary Technician		C
American Sign Language	A	
Architecture		
Architectural CAD		C
Architecture Drafting	A	
Automotive		
Auto Brakes and Wheel Alignment		C
Auto Engine Overhaul		C
Auto Tune-up and Emission Control		C
Automotive Heating, Ventilating, and Air Conditioning		C
Automotive Management		C
Automotive Power Trains		C
Basic and Advanced Clean Air Car Course		C
Industrial Technology, Automotive Option	A	
Business Administration		
Accounting	A	
Administrative Office Assistant	A	
Bookkeeping		C
Business Administration	A	
General Business		C
Office Assistant		C
Retail Management		C
Child Development		
Child Development and Family Relations	A	
Child Development Assistant Teacher		C
Child Development Associate Teacher		C
Child Development Master Teacher: Infant Toddler		C
Child Development Master Teacher: Special Education		C
Child Development Teacher		C
Early Childhood Education	A	
Communication	A	C
Computer Science		
CompTIA		C
Computer Science	A	
Software Development		C
Web Development		C
Construction		
Construction Technology		C
Industrial Technology, Construction Option	A	
Correctional Administration		
Administration of Justice	A	
Correctional Administration	A	
Criminal Justice	A	
Electronics Technology		
Electronics-Industrial Maintenance		C
Electronics-Manufacturing Automation		C
Electronics Technology	A	C
Industrial Automation		C
Industrial Communication		C
Emergency Medical Technician		C
Engineering		
Engineering	A	
Engineering Technology	A	
Fire Technology		
Chief Officer Certification		C
Fire Officer Certification		C
Fire Technology	A	C
Wildland Fire Technology	A	
Foods/Nutrition		
Child Nutrition Management Programs	A	C
Culinary Arts	A	C
Dietetic Services Supervisor Program		C
Food Services Management	A	
Human Services	A	C
Industrial Drawing		
AutoCad		C
Industrial Drawing	A	
Industrial Technology, Industrial Drawing Option	A	
Industrial Technology	A	
Journalism	A	
Kinesiology	A	

A—Associate Degree Program C—Certificate Program

BAKERSFIELD COLLEGE (continued)

Manufacturing/Machine Technology		
Basic Machine Tool Operation-Lathe, Mill		C
Computer Numerical Control Programming		C
Industrial Technology: Manufacturing Technology	A	
Manufacturing Technology		C
Nursing		
LVN to Associate Degree Nursing Program	A	
Nurse Assistant		C
Nursing	A	
Vocational Nursing Programs		C
Radiologic Technology		
Principles of Fluoroscopy		C
Principles of Venipuncture		C
Radiologic Technology	A	
Theatre Arts	A	
Welding		
Blueprint Reading & Layout for Welders		C
Gas Metal Arc/Gas Tungsten Arc Welding/ Flux Core Arc Welding		C
Industrial Technology Welding Option	A	
Shielded Metal Arc Welding		C
Welding		C
Woodworking/Cabinetmaking		
Cabinetmaking		C
Industrial Technology, Woodworking and Cabinetmaking Option	A	
Woodworking/Cabinetmaking		C

A—Associate Degree Program C—Certificate Program

BARSTOW COLLEGE

2700 Barstow Rd
Barstow CA 92311-9984
760-252-2411
760-252-1875 Fax
www.barstow.edu

Sandi Thomas, Dean of Instruction, CTE/Workforce and Economic Development

Enrollment: Full-time 789 Part-time 2,440

Semester system, summer sessions

No Housing

OCCUPATIONAL PROGRAMS

Accounting	A	C
Administration of Justice-Correction	A	C
Administration of Justice-Law Enforcement	A	C
Administrative Assistant		C
Automotive Technology	A	C
Business	A	
Child Development	A	
Child Development I		C
Child Development II		C
Child Development III		C
Computer Science	A	
Cosmetology	A	C
Diesel Technology	A	C
Family Daycare		C
Fire Technology	A	
Information Systems Management		C
Law Enforcement		C
Management	A	C
Photography	A	C
Residential Electrical	A	C
Warehousing (logistics)	A	C
Welding	A	C

A—Associate Degree Program C—Certificate Program

BERKELEY CITY COLLEGE

2050 Center St
Berkeley CA 94704-5102
510-981-2800
510-841-7333 Fax
www.berkeleycitycollege.edu

Tram Vo-Kumamoto, Vice President of Instruction

Enrollment: Full-time 1,560 Part-time 6,252

Semester system, 6 week summer session

No Housing

OCCUPATIONAL PROGRAMS

American Sign Language	A	C
American Sign Language Interpreter Training		C
Biotechnology	A	C
Business	A	C
Accounting	A	C
Business Administration	A	
Office Technology	A	
Administrative Assistant		C
Administrative/Accounting Assistant		C
Administrative Assistant/Medical		C
Computer Information System (CIS)		
Advanced Computer Programming		C
Applied Micro Computer Information Systems	A	C
Computer Application		C
Computer Programming		C
Web Programming	A	C
Web Scripting		C
Windows Desktop		C
Multimedia Arts		
Animation	A	C
Digital Imaging	A	C
Digital Video Arts	A	C
Web Design/Production	A	C
Writing for Multimedia	A	C
Public and Human Services		
Community and Public Services	A	C
Community Health Worker	A	C
Social Services Paraprofessional	A	C
Public and Human Services Cohort I		C
Public and Human Services Cohort II		C
Spanish Medical Interpreter		C

A—Associate Degree Program C—Certificate Program

BUTTE COLLEGE

3536 Butte Campus Dr
Oroville CA 95965-8399
530-895-2511
530-895-2962 Fax
www.butte.edu

Semester System, 6/8 week summer session

Mike Dunbaugh, Dean Career and Technical Programs
Denise Adams, Directory of Health Occupations
Kam Bull, Dean of Art/Family & Consumer Science
Rudy Flores, Dean of Business Education

Enrollment: Full-time 4,317 Part-time 7,894

Dormitories 25 miles away with bus service

OCCUPATIONAL PROGRAMS

Program	A	C
Accounting		
Accounting	A	C
Accounting-Account Clerk		C
Accounting-Tax Preparer		C
Administration of Justice	A	C
Agricultural Business	A	C
Agriculture/Natural Resources	A	
Agriculture Science	A	
Applied Computer Graphics		
Production/Art Studio	A	
Production/Communication Design	A	
Technical/Art Studio	A	
Technical/Art Communication Design	A	
Automotive Technology	A	C
Business		
Administration	A	
Business on the Web		C
Human Resources		C
Management		C
Retail Management		C
Small Business Institute		C
Small Business/Entrepreneurship	A	
Ceramics	A	C
Child Development	A	
Civil Engineering Technology	A	C
Communication Studies	A	C
Computer Applications	A	C
Computer-Basic Computer Competency		C
Computer Networking	A	C
Computer Networking-Cisco Network Administration		C
Computer Programming	A	C
Computer Science	A	
Computer System Administration	A	c
Computer System Administration-Microsoft Server Administration		C
Cosmetology		
Cosmetology	A	C
Esthetician		C
Manicuring		C
Court Personnel - Prelaw	A	C
Criminal Justice	A	
Criminal Justice-Administration of Justice	A	
Drafting and CAD Technology	A	C
Architectural Drafting and Modeling		C
Mechanical Applications		C
Early Childhood Education	A	C
Emergency Medical Technician 1		C
Emergency Medical Technician (EMT)-Paramedic	A	C
Environmental Horticulture	A	C
Landscape/Turfgrass Technician		C
Nursery/Florist Technician		C
Plant Protection		C
Environmental Science	A	C
Fashion Merchandising	A	C
Clothing Construction		C
Fashion Design		C
Fire Technology		C
Graphic Design for Print	A	
Heavy Equipment Operator/Technician		C
Interior Design	A	C
Kinesiology	A	
Law Enforcement-Academy Basic	A	
Law Enforcement-Academy-Basic/Fish and Game Emphasis	A	C
Leadership and Civic Engagement		C
Legal Office Administration	A	C
Legal Office Administration-Basic Computer Competency		C
Marketing	A	C
Business on the Web		C
Mechanized Agriculture	A	C
Medical Office Administration	A	C
Basic Computer Competence		C
Multimedia Studies	A	C
Natural Resource Management	A	
Ecological Restoration		C
Parks and Recreation		C
Wildlife Technician		C

A—Associate Degree Program C—Certificate Program

BUTTE COLLEGE continued

Nursing		
Acute Care Nurse Assistant		C
Certified Nursing Assistant		C
Home Health Aide		C
LVN	A	C
Registered–LVN to ADN	A	C
Nutrition and Food Science	A	
Basic Computer Competence		C
Photography	A	
Radio-TV Film: Video Production	A	C
Real Estate	A	C
Appraisal		C
Sales		C
Recording Arts for Musicians		C
Respiratory Care	A	C
Sustainability Studies		C
Theatre Arts	A	C
Visual Merchandising	A	C
Welding Technology	A	C
Level I		C
Level II		C
Level III		C
PowerPathway Gas Pipeline Welding		C

A—Associate Degree Program C—Certificate Program

CABRILLO COLLEGE

6500 Soquel Dr
Aptos CA 95003-3119
831-479-6201
831-479-5782 Fax
www.cabrillo.edu

Semester system, One 6 week summer session

Rock Pfotenhauer, Dean of Instruction, Career Education and Economic Development

Enrollment: Total 15,541

No Housing

OCCUPATIONAL PROGRAMS

Accounting/Finance		
Accounting	A	C
Bookkeeping		C
Business		
General Business	A	C
Computer and Information Systems:		
Cisco Certified Networking Associate (CCNA)		C
Cisco Certified Networking Professional (CCNP)		C
Computer Networking and System Administration:	A	C
Microsoft System Administration		C
UNIX/Linux System Administration		C
Computer Applications/Business Technology		
Administrative Support		C
Computer/Business Applications	A	C
Computer Skills		C
Professional Computer Applications		C
Computer Science:	A	
C++ Programming		C
Game Programming		C
Java Programming		C
Programming		C
Web Programming		C
Computer Support Specialist:	A	
A+ Preparation		C
Computer Support Technician 1		C
Construction and Energy Management	A	C
Building Inspection and Construction Codes	A	C
Construction Basics		C
Construction Building Inspection and Codes		C
Construction Business Management		C
Construction Career Path		C
Construction Electrical Inspection and Codes		C
Construction Project Management		C
Construction Specialty Inspection and Codes		C
Construction Trade		C
Solar Derived Energy Management		C
Culinary Arts and Hospitality Management	A	C
Entry Level Baking		C
Entry Level Catering		C
Entry Level Cook		C
Wine Tasting Room Management		C
World Wines		C
Dental Hygiene	A	
Digital Management and Career Preparation		
Preparation for Leadership and Management Careers		C
Digital Media		
Digital Publishing	A	C
Graphic Imaging		C
Motion Media		C
Publication Design		C
Web Design		C
Web Development		C
Web Media	A	C
Web Production		C
Early Childhood Education	A	
Anti-Bias Curriculum		C
Bilingual Spanish English Teaching		C
Curriculum Planning		C
ECE Administration		C
ECE Children's Literacy Curriculum		C
Infant/Toddler Care		C
Proficiency in Teaching		C
Spanish/English Early Childhood Teaching		C
Working with Diverse Families		C
Engineering Technology	A	C
Architectural Drafting and Design		C
Civil/Survey Drafting		C
Computer Aided Drafting and Design		C
Computer Animation		C
Manufacturing Specialist		C
Technology and Trades		C
Horticulture		
Arboriculture		C
General Horticulture		C
General Horticulture and Crop Production	A	C
Greenhouse and Nursery Management		C
Landscape Design		C
Landscape Horticulture	A	C
Landscaping		C
Permaculture		C
Sustainable and Organic Food Production		C

A—Associate Degree Program C—Certificate Program

CABRILLO COLLEGE (continued)

Human Services	A	
Drug and Alcohol Studies		C
Generalist Practice		C
Journalism	A	C
Medical Assistant	A	C
Electronic Health Records		C
Phlebotomy Technician		C
Nursing	A	
Public Safety		
Administration of Justice	A	
Criminal Justice: Corrections	A	
Criminal Justice: Law Enforcement	A	
Emergency Medical Technician		C
Fire Service Management	A	C
Fire Technology	A	
Radiologic Technology	A	
Venipuncture		C
Welding		
Advanced Welding		C
Basic Welding		C

A—Associate Degree Program C—Certificate Program

CAÑADA COLLEGE

4200 Farm Hill Blvd
Redwood City CA 94061-1099
650-306-3100
650-306-3282 Fax
www.canadacollege.edu

Semester system, 6 week summer sessions

Dean Business, Design & Workforce

Enrollment: Full-time 1,898 Part-time 6,930

No Housing

OCCUPATIONAL PROGRAMS

Accounting	A	C
Entry Level Bookkeeper		C
Payroll Specialist		C
Business Administration	A	C
Assistant Business Administration	A	C
Computer/Business/Office Technology		
Administrative Assistant	A	C
Administrative Support Assistant	A	C
General Office		C
Computer Science		
Computer Science C++	A	C
Computer Science JAVA		C
Computer Science Objective C		C
Digital Art and Animation	A	C
3D Animation and Videogame Art	A	C
Graphic Design		C
Web Design		C
Early Childhood Education (ECE)	A	
ECE/Child Development	A	C
Elementary Teacher Education	A	
Entrepreneurship and Small Business Management	A	C
Fashion	A	C
Custom Dressmaking/Small Business	A	C
Fashion Merchandising	A	C
Technical (Apparel Industry Oriented)	A	C
Theater Costuming	A	C
Fitness Professional	A	C
Human Services	A	C
Community Health Worker		C
Promoter Education and Employment Project		C
Interior Design	A	C
Home Staging		C
Kitchen & Bath		C
Residential and Commercial Design		C
Sustainable Design		C
Medical Assisting	A	C
Medical Administrative Assistant		C
Medical Billing Specialist	A	C
Medical Coding Specialist		C
Paralegal	A	C
Radiologic Technology	A	

A—Associate Degree Program   C—Certificate Program

COLLEGE OF THE CANYONS

26455 Rockwell Canyon Rd
Santa Clarita CA 91355-1899
661-259-7800
661-259-3043 Fax
www.canyons.edu

Semester System, 5 and 8 week Summer Session, 5 week Winter Intersession

Audrey Green, Associate Vice President of Academic Affairs

Enrollment: Full-time 6,601 Part-time 10,277

No Housing

OCCUPATIONAL PROGRAMS

Program	A	C
Administration of Justice	A	C
Animation		
Animation Production	A	C
Computer Animation	A	C
Video Game Animation		C
Athletic Training	A	
Automotive Technology	A	C
Biotechnology		C
Business	A	C
Accounting Technician	A	C
Accounting (Transfer)	A	C
Customer Service		C
E-Commerce/Business		C
Entrepreneurship and Small Business Management	A	C
Finance		C
Human Resources Management	A	C
International Trade–Finance		C
International Trade–Marketing		C
Marketing	A	C
Restaurant Entrepreneur		C
Retail Management		C
Communication Studies	A	
Computer Information Technology		
Administrative Assistant	A	C
Computer Applications	A	C
E-Commerce/Technology		C
Medical Office Administrative Assistant		C
Web-Site Development		C
Computer Networking	A	C
Network Associate		C
Computer Science	A	
Construction Management	A	C
Building Inspection		C
Culinary Arts		C
Baking & Pastry		C
Drafting		
Architectural Drafting	A	C
Early Child Education	A	
Core		C
Infant/Toddler		C
Preschool		C
School Age		C
Special Education		C
Supervision/Administration		C
Engineering	A	
Mechanical Drawing		C
Fire Technology		
In-Service	A	
Pre-Service	A	C
Gerontology		
Skills for Healthy Aging Resources and Programs (SHARP)		C
Health Science		
Emergency Medical Technician I		C
Hotel/Restaurant Management	A	
Hotel Management	A	
Restaurant Management	A	
Interior Design	A	C
Home Staging		C
Interior Decorating and Merchandising		C
Set Decorator		C
Kinesiology	A	
Personal Trainer		C
Sports Medicine	A	
Land Surveying	A	C
Manufacturing Technology		
Automated Machining		C
CAD/CAM		C
CATIA		C
Machining/CNC		C
Media Entertainment Arts		
Animation Production	A	C
Computer Animation	A	C
Filmmaking	A	
New Media Journalism	A	
News Reporting and Anchoring		C
Sound Arts	A	
Video Game Animation		C

A—Associate Degree Program C—Certificate Program

COLLEGE OF THE CANYONS (continued)

Medical Lab Technician	A	
Nursing		
Certified Nurse Assistant		C
LVN to RN Career Ladder	A	
Registered Nurse RN	A	
Paralegal	A	
Photography		
Commercial Photography		C
Fine Art Photography	A	C
Real Estate	A	C
Recreation Management	A	
Sign Language		
American Sign Language Interpreting	A	
Solar Energy Technician		C
Sustainable Design and Development		C
Water Systems Technology	A	C
Welding	A	C
Robotic Welding Automation		C
Shielded Metal Arc Welding (SMAW)		C
Wine Studies		C
Hospitality Wine Service		C

CERRITOS COLLEGE

11110 Alondra Blvd
Norwalk CA 90650-6298
562-860-2451
562-467-5005 Fax
www.cerritos.edu

Rich Miranda, Dean of Academic Affairs

Enrollment: Full-time 5,030 Part-time 17,425

Semester System; 6, 8, & 12 Week Summer Sessions

No Housing

OCCUPATIONAL PROGRAMS

Accounting	A	C
Advanced Accounting	A	C
Advanced Microcomputer Accounting Clerk	A	C
Microcomputer Accounting Clerk	A	C
Payroll Administration	A	C
Administration of Justice	A	
Architectural Technology	A	C
Automotive Collision Repair	A	
General Automotive Collision Repair		C
Automotive Mechanical Repair	A	
Alternate Fuels Service Technician		C
Automatic Management		C
Engine/Diagnosis Technician		C
Engine/Machining Technology		C
General Technology		C
Manufacture Specialty		C
Business Administration	A	C
Business Management	A	C
Business Marketing	A	C
Human Resources Management	A	C
International Business	A	C
Retail Management	A	C
Small Business Management/Entrepreneurship	A	C
Business Communications Office Technology		
General Office	A	C
Legal Secretary	A	C
Secretary/Administrative Assistant	A	C
Word Processing	A	C
Child Development/Early Childhood	A	C
Associate Teacher Specialization	C	
Child Development/Preschool Director		C
Child Development/Special Education		C
Infant/Toddler Teacher		C
School-Age Child Care		C
Computer and Information Science	A	C
iSeries 400 Specialist		C
Microcomputer Specialist	A	C
Networking Technicians/Operators	A	C
Operator	A	C
Programmer	A	C
Information Sciences System Analyst	A	C

Computer Science	A	C
Cosmetology	A	C
Esthetician	A	C
Court Reporting and Captioning Careers	A	
Hearing Reporter		C
Proofreader-Court Reporting Methods		C
Realtime Rapid Text Entry		C
Scopist for Court Reporters	C	
Culinary Arts	A	C
Chef's Training		C
Professional Baking and Pastry		C
Dental Assisting	A	C
Dental Hygiene	A	
Digital Arts	A	
Computer Animation		C
Motion Graphics		C
Engineering	A	
Engineering Design Technology	A	C
Industrial Technology	A	
Insurance—Property and Casualty		C
Interpreting/Translating		C
Machine Tool Technology	A	C
Machinist Option	A	C
Numerical Control Machine Operator Option	A	C
Numerical Control Tool Major Requirement Option	A	C
Tool and Die Maker Option	A	C
Mass Communications		
Broadcast Media	A	
Journalism	A	C
Medical Assistant	A	C
Mental Health Worker	A	C
Music		
Commercial Music	A	
New Product Development	A	C
Nursing		
Option A—Associate in Arts Degree	A	
Option B—LPT-ADN Mobility Major	A	
Option C—LVN-ADN Mobility Major	A	
Option D—LVN-30 Unit Option	A	
Pharmacy Technician	A	C

A—Associate Degree Program C—Certificate Program

CERRITOS COLLEGE (continued)

Physical Education		
Exercise Science: Athletic Trainer Aide	A	C
Exercise Science: Fitness Specialist	A	C
Physical Therapist Assistant	A	
Plastics/Composites Manufacturing Technology (PMT)	A	C
Real Estate	A	C
Speech-Language Pathology Aide		C
Speech-Language Pathology Assistant		C
Welding	A	C
Woodworking Manufacturing Technologies	A	C
Cabinetmaking		C
Furniture Making		C

A—Associate Degree Program C—Certificate Program

CERRO COSO COMMUNITY COLLEGE

3000 College Heights Blvd
Ridgecrest CA 93555-9571
760-384-6100
760-375-4776 Fax
www.cerrocoso.edu

Semester system, 6 & 8 week summer session

Mike McNair, Dean of Instruction and Career Technology Education

Enrollment: Full-time 700 Part-time 5,600

No Housing

OCCUPATIONAL PROGRAMS

Administration of Justice	A	C
Business	A	C
Business Administration	A	
Business Management	A	C
Small Business Management/Entrepreneurship	A	C
Business Office Technology	A	C
Child Development	A	C
Assistant Teacher		C
Associate Teacher		C
Master Teacher Permit		C
Site Supervisor Permit		C
Teacher		C
Computer Information Systems	A	C
Computer Technology	A	C
Engineering Technology	A	C
Health Careers		
Administrative Medical Assistant		C
Clinical Medical Assistant		C
Medical Assistant		C
Medical Assisting Externship		C
Human Services	A	C
Human Services Worker		C
Industrial Technology	A	C
Machine Tool Technology	A	C
Management/Entrepreneur	A	C
Paralegal Studies	A	
Vocational Nursing	A	C
Web Design	A	C
Digital Media Skills		C
Welding Technology	A	C

A—Associate Degree Program C—Certificate Program

CHABOT COLLEGE

25555 Hesperian Blvd
Hayward CA 94545-5001
510-723-6600
510-782-9315 Fax
www.chabotcollege.edu

Semester System, Summer Session

Vacant, Dean–Applied Technology and Business

Enrollment: Full-time 3,325 Part-time 11,823

No Housing

OCCUPATIONAL PROGRAMS

Program	A	C
Accounting	A	
Accounting Technician		C
Administration of Justice	A	
Administrative Assistant	A	C
Administrative Assistant Entrepreneur		C
Aquatics		C
Architecture	A	C
Automotive Technology	A	
Chassis Technology		C
Drivetrain Technology		C
Emphasis in BMW Manufacture Training	A	
Engine Machining		C
Engine Performance Technology		C
Maintenance Technology		C
Technology Entrepreneur		C
Bookkeeping		C
Business		
Emphasis, Management	A	
Emphasis, Marketing	A	
Business Administration	A	
Business Graphics		C
Business Skills		C
Coaching		C
Computer Science	A	
Emphasis in Mathematics	A	
Consumer Technology		C
Entrepreneur		C
Dental Hygiene	A	
Digital Design		C
Digital Media		C
Early Childhood Development	A	
Associate Teacher		C
Basic Teacher		C
Early Childhood Intervention	A	
Assistant		C
Electronic Systems Technology	A	
Engineering	A	
Entrepreneurship		C
Environmental Studies	A	
Fire Technology	A	C
Prevention Inspector	A	C
Fitness Instructor		C
Geographic Information System (GIS)		C
Graphic Design	A	C
Health Care Management		C
Human Resources Assistant		C
Human Services	A	
Illustration		C
Industrial Electronic Technology		C
Industrial Technology	A	
Inspection and Pipe Welding		C
Interior Design	A	C
International Studies	A	
Journalism	A	
Kinesiology	A	
Kitchen and Bath Design		C
Machine Tool Technology	A	
Machinist		C
Management		C
Marketing		C
Mass Communication	A	
Medical Assisting	A	C
Music	A	
Industry Entrepreneur		C
Numerical Control	A	
Numerical Control Programmer (Machinist)		C
Nursing	A	
Nursing Program, LVN to RN	A	
Office Technology		C
Personal Fitness Training Entrepreneur		C
Photography	A	C
Project Management		C
Radio and Television Broadcasting	A	
Real Estate	A	C
Real Estate Entrepreneur		C
Retailing		C
Retail Management	A	C
Small Business Management		C
Software Specialist	A	C
Sports Injury Care		C
Theatre Arts	A	
Tool Maker		C
Welding		C
Welding Technology	A	

A—Associate Degree Program C—Certificate Programs

CHAFFEY COLLEGE

5885 Haven Ave
Rancho Cucamonga CA 91737-3002
909-652-6000
909-652-6228 Fax
www.chaffey.edu

Semester System; Weekend College; 6 & 9 week Summer Sessions

Joy Haerens, Director, Economic and Community Development

Enrollment: Full-time 4,635 Part-time 11,781

No Housing

OCCUPATIONAL PROGRAMS

Accounting/Financial Services	A	C
Bookkeeping		C
Financial Planning		C
Government and Not-for-Profit Organizations		C
Paraprofessional		C
Payroll and Income Tax Preparer		C
Administration of Justice	A	C
Art/Digital Media		
Computer Graphic for Print Media Emphasis	A	C
Design for Multimedia Emphasis	A	C
Illustration Emphasis	A	C
Web Design Emphasis	A	C
Automotive Technology	A	C
Automotive Electrical Systems		C
General Automotive Service Technician	A	C
Master Automotive Technician	A	C
Engine Performance (Smog Check) Technician		C
Engine Rebuilding		C
High Performance Engines Building & Blueprinting		C
Aviation Maintenance Technology	A	C
Airframe	A	C
Powerplant	A	C
Broadcasting & Cinema	A	C
Business Administration	A	C
Marketing		C
Small Business Entrepreneur, Levels I & II	A	C
Business: Management	A	C
Logistics Management	A	C
Management—Levels I & II		C
Retail Management	A	C
Supervision—Levels I & II	A	C
Business: Paralegal Studies		C
Business and Office Technologies:		
Data Entry		C
General Office Assistant: Levels I & II		C
Microsoft Office Excel Application		C
Microsoft Office Expert		C
Microsoft Office Specialist		C
Microsoft Word Specialist		C
Office Management	A	C
Professional Administrative Assistant: Executive	A	C
Professional Administrative Assistant: Executive/Bilingual	A	C
Professional Administrative Assistant: Medical	A	C
Computer Information Systems	A	C
Cisco (CCNA) Exam Preparation, Level I-IV		C
Cisco (CCNP) Exam Preparation, Level V-IX		C
Correctional Science	A	C
Culinary Arts/Food Service		
Culinary Arts		C
Food Production		C
Food Service/Waitstaff/Personnel	A	C
Dental Assisting	A	C
Drafting		
Architectural	A	C
Mechanical	A	C
Education Paraprofessional	A	C
Education Paraprofessional, Level I and II		C
Fashion Design and Merchandising		
Costume Design	A	C
Custom Dressmaking		C
Fashion Design	A	C
Fashion Merchandising	A	C
Industrial Sewing		C
Patternmaking for Apparel		C
Fire Technology: Professional Firefighter		C
Gerontology	A	C
Community Caregiver		C
Hotel Management	A	C
Industrial Electrical Technology		
Electromechanical Technology Levels I, II, & III	A	C
Fiber Optic Cabling Technician		C
Industrial Electrical Technology Levels I, II, & III	A	C
Instrumentation Technology Level I & II	A	C
Networking Cabling Technician		C
Interior Design	A	C
Journalism		C
Nursing		
Acute Care Technician		C
Home Health Aide		C
Nursing Assistant		C
Vocational Nursing	A	C

A—Associate Degree Program C—Certificate Program

CHAFFEY COLLEGE (continued)

Nutrition and Food		
Dietetic Service Supervisor		C
Nutrition and Food	A	C
Pharmacy Technician	A	C
Photography		
Still Photography		C
Physical Education		
Coaching		C
Radiologic Technology	A	

A—Associate Degree Program C—Certificate Program

CITRUS COLLEGE

1000 West Foothill Blvd
Glendora CA 91741-1899
626-852-6402
www.citruscollege.edu

Semester System and Short Term Classes; 8 Week Summer Session, 6 Week Winter Session

James Lancaster, Dean, Career and Technical Education

Enrollment: Full & Part-time 13,000

No Housing

OCCUPATIONAL PROGRAMS

Administration of Justice	A	C
Audio Recording Technology	A	C
Automotive Technology	A	C
Business	A	C
Child Development	A	C
Cosmetology/Esthetician	A	C
Dental Assisting	A	C
Design and Drafting Technology	A	C
Emergency Medical Technician		C
Information Technology	A	C
Nursing		
ADN/RN	A	C
Vocational	A	C
Office Technology		C
Public Works	A	C
Theatre: Emerging Theatre Technology (ETT)	A	C
Water Technology	A	C
Wildland Resources/Forestry		C

A—Associate Degree Program C—Certificate Program

COASTLINE COMMUNITY COLLEGE

11460 Warner Ave
Fountain Valley CA 92708-2597
714-546-7600
714-241-6187 Fax
www.coastline.edu

Nancy Jones, Dean of Instruction, Career and Technical Programs

Enrollment: Full-time 1,097 Part-time 10,863

Semester system; 8 week summer session

No Housing

OCCUPATIONAL PROGRAMS

Program	A	C
Accounting	A	C
Advanced		C
Bookkeeping	A	C
General	A	C
Intermediate		C
Taxation	A	C
Biological Laboratory Technician		C
Building Codes Technology		
Combination Building Inspection	A	C
Combination Residential Inspection	A	C
Code Professional	A	C
Green Building Technology	A	C
Permit Technician	A	C
Business	A	
Business Administration	A	C
Business Plan		C
General	A	C
Human Resource Management	A	C
Marketing	A	C
Business Management		
Business Plan		C
Entrepreneurship and Small Business Management	A	C
Home Business		C
Project Management		C
Retail Management	A	C
Supply Chain Management	A	C
Cognitive and Caregiver Boot Camp		C
Computer Networking	A	C
Cisco	A	C
Cisco Certified Networking Administrator (CCNA)		C
Cisco Certified Networking Professional (CCNP)		C
CompTIA		C
MCSA: Windows 8		C
MCSA: Windows Server 2012		C
Microsoft® Concentration	A	
Network Security		C
Security Concentration	A	C
Windows Server 2008		C
Digital Media Foundation		C
Animation and Gaming Foundation		C
Motion Graphic		C
Print Design		C
Web Design		C
Web Technologies		C
Electronics	A	C
Gerontology	A	C
Health Care Management	A	C
Informatics	A	C
Leadership		C
Management and Supervision		
Home Business		C
Management	A	C
Supervision and Management	A	C
Medical Administrative Office Technician		C
Medical Coding Specialist		C
Office Support Specialist		
Administrative Manager	A	C
Administrative Professional (Assistant)	A	C
Financial Assistant	A	C
Financial Manager	A	C
General Office Assistant		C
General Office Manager	A	C
Paralegal Studies	A	C
Physical Education and Health	A	
Health and Fitness	A	
Process Technology	A	C
Process Technician Fundamentals		C
Real Estate		
Broker		C
Lending and Mortgage Brokering		C
Property Salesperson		C
Studies		C

A—Associate Degree Program C—Certificate Program

COLUMBIA COLLEGE

11600 Columbia College Dr
Sonora CA 95370-8580
209-588-5100
209-588-5104 Fax
www.gocolumbia.edu

Leslie Buckalew, Vice President for Instruction;
Kathy Sullivan, Interim Dean of Instructional Services, Career Technical Education

Enrollment: 3415 full-time and part-time

Semester system; summer sessions varying in length

Student Housing Complex

OCCUPATIONAL PROGRAMS

Automotive Technology	A	C
Automotive Maintenance Technician	A	C
Automotive Service Technician	A	C
Engine Performance		C
Under Vehicle Service		C
Business Administration	A	
Accounting	A	C
Accounting Clerk		C
Management	A	C
Organizational Behavior		C
Payroll Clerk		C
Small Business Management		C
Tax Clerk		C
Child Development	A	
Associate Child Development Teacher		C
Early Childhood Education	A	
Computer Science		C
Computer Graphics		C
Computer Information System		C
Digital Media		C
Geographic Information Systems (GIS)		C
Emergency Medical Service	A	C
Entrepreneurship	A	C
Virtual Office Professional		C
Fire Technology	A	C
Woodland/Urban Interface Fire Management	A	
Forestry and Natural Resources	A	C
Hospitality Management		
Culinary Arts	A	C
Hotel Management	A	C
Restaurant Management	A	C
Multimedia Technology	A	
Digital Graphics Arts		C
Multimedia Technician-Digital Media		C
Multimedia Technician-Web Development		C
Multimedia Web Design		C
Website Development		C
Office Technology		
Administrative Office Professional	A	
Medical Office Specialist	A	C
Office Professional		C
Virtual Office Professional		C
Water Resources Management	A	C
Wastewater Treatment Plant Operation		C
Welding Technology, Level I, II, III		C

A—Associate Degree Program C—Certificate Program

CONTRA COSTA COLLEGE

2600 Mission Bell Dr
San Pablo CA 94806-3195
510-235-7800
510-236-6768 Fax
www.contracosta.edu

Semester system; 6 & 8 week summer sessions and intersessions

Donna Floyd, Senior Dean, Economic Development

Enrollment: Full-time 3,000 Part-time 6,000

No Housing

OCCUPATIONAL PROGRAMS

Program	A	C
Administration of Justice		
Correctional Specialist		C
Corrections	A	C
Forensic Criminalist		C
Investigative Specialist		C
Law Enforcement	A	C
Patrol Specialist		C
Police and Correctional Academy Readiness		C
Police Services Specialist		C
Security Specialist		C
Automotive Services		
Auto Collision Repair Technology	A	C
Body and Mechanical		C
Body and Refinishing		C
Damage Estimator		C
Auto Mechanics	A	C
Auto Collision Repair and Body Mechanical		C
Brake, Steering and Suspension Technician		C
Electrical Technician		C
Engine Technician		C
Heating and Air Conditioning Technician		C
Business		
Accounting Technician		C
Business Administration	A	C
Business Management	A	C
Computer and Communication Technology		
Alternate Energy Technologies		C
Basic Electronics		C
Computer and Communication Technologies		C
Computer Repair Technology		C
Digital Applications and Devices		C
Fiber Optic/Copper Networking Structure		C
Independent Study		C
Network Communication Technology		C
Network Technology	A	C
Security Systems for Home and Small Business		C
Wireless Networks for Home and Small Business		C
Computer Information Systems		
Computer Operations	A	C
Computer Programming	A	C
Computer Science	A	
Culinary Arts		
Basic Food Service		C
Classical/Modern Food Preparation and Restaurant Training	A	C
Pastry and Baking Skills	A	C
Restaurant Management		C
Engineering	A	C
Graphic Arts		
Digital Art and Design	A	
Health and Human Services		
Dual Diagnosis Screening		C
Dual Diagnosis Specialization		C
Human Services	A	C
Peer Support Services		C
Psychosocial Rehabilitation		C
Substance Abuse Case Management		C
Journalism	A	C
Medical Assisting and Office Technology	A	C
Medical Terminology		C
Nursing	A	
Physical Education/Kinesiology	A	
Baseball Officiating		C
Fitness Trainer		C
Personal Training Prep Course		C
Real Estate	A	C

A—Associate Degree Program C—Certificate Program

COPPER MOUNTAIN COLLEGE

6162 Rotary Way
Joshua Tree CA 92252
760-366-3791
760-366-5255 Fax
www.cmccd.edu

Semester system; Summer session

Pamela Kersey, Dean for Instruction

Enrollment: Full-time 1,400 Part-time 2,100

No housing

OCCUPATIONAL PROGRAMS

Automotive Technology	A	
Business		
Accounting		C
Bookkeeping		C
Business Administration	A	
Economics	A	
General Business		C
Office Assistant		C
Child Development	A	
Associate Teacher		C
Early Childhood Education	A	
Master Teacher		C
Teacher		C
Communications	A	
Computer Information Systems	A	C
Graphic Design Technology		C
Photoshop with Animation		C
Web Design		C
Computer Science	A	
Computer Programing	A	C
Criminal Justice	A	
Culinary Arts		C
Fire Technology	A	C
Health Sciences		
Emergency Medical Technician		C
Home Health Aide		C
Nurse Assistant		C
Registered Nursing	A	
Vocational Nursing	A	C

A—Associate Degree Program C—Certificate Program

COSUMNES RIVER COLLEGE

8401 Center Prkwy
Sacramento CA 95823-5799
916-691-7344
916-691-7375 Fax
www.crc.losrios.edu

Condensed calendar 16 weeks: 1st 8 week, 2nd 8 week, 6 & 8 week summer sessions

Cory Wathen, Vice President, Administrative Services and Student Support

Enrollment: Day 12,107 Evening 1,091

No Housing

OCCUPATIONAL PROGRAMS

Accounting	A	C
Advanced		C
Clerk		C
Taxation Certificate		C
Advertising/Public Relations	A	
Agriculture Business	A	C
Agriculture, General	A	C
Architectural Design Technology		
Building Information Modeling	A	C
Interior Information Modeling	A	C
Architecture Technology	A	C
Green Buildings: Environmental Design		
Energy Management and Performance Based Construction		C
Art		
Design	A	
Photography	A	
Automotive Mechanics Technology	A	C
Automatic Transmissions/Transaxles		C
Brakes		C
Electrical Systems		C
Emission Control		C
Engine Performance		C
Engine Repair		C
Heating and Air Conditioning		C
Small Engine Repair		C
Suspension and Steering		C
Broadcast Journalism	A	
Building Inspection Technology	A	C
Concrete Construction Inspection		C
Business		
Administrative Professional		C
Business Administration	A	
E-Business and the Internet		C
General	A	
Office Assistant		C
Office Technician		C
Small Business Management/Entrepreneurship	A	C
Communication/Organizational	A	
Communications Studies		
Applied Communication Skills		C

Computer Information Science	A	
Application Specialist		C
Computer Programmer–SQL		C
Computer Programming	A	C
Database Analyst-SQL		C
Database Design		C
Desktop Publishing		C
Enterprise Administrator	A	C
Information Systems Security	A	C
Internet Programming		C
Linux Systems Administrator		C
Management Information Systems	A	
Application Expert		C
Application Specialist		C
Application Master		C
Network Helpdesk Technician		C
Programming in C/C++		C
Relational Database Administration		C
Server Administrator	A	C
Software Development using Visual BASIC.NET		C
Software Development with JAVA		C
Web Programming		C
Web Publishing		C
Construction	A	C
Building Performance and Energy Assessment	A	C
Construction, Pre-Apprenticeship		C
Construction Management Technology	A	C
Culinary Arts Management	A	
Basic Culinary Services		C
Community Nutrition Specialist		C
Cooking and Supervision		C
School Food Service Specialist		C
Diagnostic Medical Sonography	A	C
Digital Media	A	C
Early Childhood Education	A	C
Associate Teacher		C
Infant Specialist		C
Home Early Care and Education		C
Master Teacher		C
Master Teacher Specialization Options		C
School Age Child Care and Education		C

A—Associate Degree Program C—Certificate Program

COSUMNES RIVER COLLEGE (continued)

Site Supervisor	A	
Teacher		C
Engineering	A	
Equine Science	A	
Film and Media Studies	A	
Finance	A	
Fire Technology	A	C
Geography	A	
Environmental Studies and Sustainability	A	
Professional Application of Geographic Information System (GIS)		C
Geology	A	
Health	A	
Health Information Technology	A	
Health Information Coding Specialist		C
Horticulture		
Landscape Technology	A	C
Nursery Management	A	
Nursery Operations		C
Sustainable Irrigation and Water Management Technology		C
Sustainable Landscape and Irrigation System Design	A	
Human Services	A	C
Chemical Dependency Studies	A	C
Journalism-Communication Media	A	
Management	A	
Retail Management		C
Marketing	A	
Medical Assisting	A	C
Administrative		C
Medical Insurance Billing		C
Nutrition & Foods	A	
Community Nutrition		C
Pharmacy Technology	A	
Photography	A	C
Commercial and Studio Photography		C
Portraiture and Wedding Photography		C
Radio Production	A	C
Television Production	A	C
Real Estate	A	
Broker		C
Sales		C
Theater Arts	A	
Theater for Young Audiences		C
Veterinary Technology	A	C

A—Associate Degree Program C—Certificate Program

CRAFTON HILLS COLLEGE

11711 Sand Canyon Rd
Yucaipa CA 92399
909-794-2161
909-794-0423 Fax
www.craftonhills.edu

June Yamamoto, Dean of Career Education and Human Development

Enrollment: Full-time 1,935 Part-time 4,269

Semester System; 6 , 7 & 8 week summer sessions

No Housing

OCCUPATIONAL PROGRAMS

Business Administration	A	
Business Management		C
Retail Management		C
Child Development	A	
Associate Teacher		C
Early Childhood Education	A	
Master Teacher		C
Site Supervisor		C
Teacher Certificate		C
Communication Studies	A	
Computer Information Systems	A	C
Cisco Certified Network Associate		C
Computer-Assisted Graphic Design		C
Programming		C
Web Design		C
Emergency Medical Services	A	
Emergency Medical Technician I/EMT Basic		C
Emergency Medical Technician–Paramedic		C
Mobile Intensive Care Nurse		C
Fire Technology	A	
California Fire Officer Training		C
Firefighter I Basic Training Academy		C
Fire Inspection Academy		C
Marketing Management		C
Radiological Technology	A	C
Respiratory Care	A	
Theatre Arts	A	

A—Associate Degree Program C—Certificate Program

CUESTA COLLEGE

P O Box 8106
San Luis Obispo CA 93403-8106
805-546-3973
805-546-3966 Fax
www.cuesta.edu

Semester system; 18 week Fall and Spring sessions, 6 week summer session

John A. Cascamo, Dean of Academic Affairs, Workforce and Economic Development

Enrollment: Full-time 5,009 Part-time 6,207

No Housing

OCCUPATIONAL PROGRAMS

Agricultural Technology	A	C
Art	A	
Graphics		C
Automotive Technology		
Advanced Engine Performance Technician	A	
Auto Body Technician	A	C
Automatic Transmission/Transaxle Specialist		C
Automotive Technician	A	
Brakes Specialist		C
Chassis and Suspension Specialist		C
Electrical Systems Specialist		C
Engine Performance Specialist		C
Engine Repair Specialist		C
Heating and Air Conditioning Specialist		C
Manual Drivetrains and Axles Specialist		C
Broadcast Communications	A	
Business		
Business Administration	A	C
Customer Service		C
Internet Digital Marketing		C
Management	A	
Marketing	A	
Computer and Networking Technology	A	
Computer A+ Repair and Administration		C
Computer Networking Specialist		C
Network Infrastructure Specialist		C
Computer Application/Office Administration	A	
Accounting Clerk/ Bookkeeper		C
Administrative Assistant		C
Computer Information Systems		
Android Developer		C
Computer Science	A	
Internet Applications Developer		C
IOS Developer		C
Management Information Systems	A	
Construction Technology	A	C
Criminal Justice	A	
Early Childhood Education	A	C
Electronics and Electrical Technology		
Electrical Technology	A	C
Power and Instrumentation Certificate		C
Emergency Medical Services		
Basic to Emergency Medical Technician (EMT) Transition		C
Paramedic	A	C
Emergency Medical Services Hazardous Materials First Responder Operational		C
Emergency Medical Services Technician		C
Emergency Medical Services Technician Refresher		C
Engineering	A	
Family Studies/Human Services		
Addiction Studies		C
Addiction Studies Field Work		C
Journalism	A	
Kinesiology		
Coaching		C
Fitness, Healthy, Nutrition	A	
Personal Training		C
Legal Studies		
Legal Studies: Business Emphasis	A	
Legal Studies: Social Science Emphasis	A	
Library/Information Technology	A	C
Library Services to Children		C
Searching and Researching Strategies		C
Web Page Coding		C
Medical Assisting	A	C
Phlebotomy		C
Music		
Audio Technology I		C
Jazz Studies	A	
Music Performance	A	
Nursing Assistant		C
Nursing, Licensed Vocational Nurse		C
Basic Intraveneous Therapy, Blood Administration, and Phlebotomy		C
Nursing, Registered	A	C
Nutrition		C
Paralegal	A	C
Psychiatric Technician	A	C
Recreation Administration	A	

A—Associate Degree Program C—Certificate Program

CUESTA COLLEGE (continued)

Welding		
Welding Pipe		C
Welding Technology	A	C
Welding Technology Structural Steel		C

A—Associate Degree Program C—Certificate Program

CUYAMACA COLLEGE

900 Rancho San Diego Parkway
El Cajon CA 92019-4304
619-660-4000
619-660-4399 Fax
www.cuyamaca.edu

Semester System: 16 week fall and spring, Summer: 4 week, 6 week, 8 week

Kate Alder, PhD, Dean, Career and Technical Education

Enrollment: Full-time 2,468 Part-time 7,496

No Housing

OCCUPATIONAL PROGRAMS

Accounting	A	C
Bookkeeping		C
Automotive Technology	A	C
Advanced Engine Performance and Emissions		C
ASEP	A	
ASSET	A	
Brakes and Front-End		C
Engine Performance and Drive Train		C
Business		
Business Administration	A	C
Business Data Management	A	C
Business—General	A	C
Database Administration		C
Business Office Technology	A	C
Account Clerk		C
Administrative Assistant	A	C
Executive Assistant	A	C
Front Office Receptionist		C
Office Assistant Level I and II		C
Office Professional		C
Office Software Specialist Level I and II		C
CADD Technology		
Building Design Industry	A	C
Manufacturing Industry	A	C
Child Development		
Early Childhood Education	A	
Infants and Toddlers	A	C
Preschool Children	A	C
Computer and Information Science		
Cisco Certified Network Associate		C
Cisco Network Professional		C
Computer Programming		C
Computer Support Technician		C
Networking, Security and System Administration	A	C
Web Design		C
Web Development	A	C
Web Programming		C
Engineering		
Civil Engineering	A	C
Electrical and Computer Engineering	A	C
Mechanical and Aerospace Engineering	A	C
Mechatronics		C
Entrepreneurship—Small Business Management	A	C
Environmental Health and Safety Management		
Environmental Management	A	
Environmental Technician		C
Occupational Safety and Health Management	A	
Occupational Safety and Health Technician		C
Graphic Design	A	C
Digital Photography		C
Web Graphics		C
Management	A	C
Ornamental Horticulture		
Arboriculture	A	C
Basic Ornamental Horticulture		C
Floral Design	A	C
Golf Course and Sports Turf Management	A	C
Irrigation Technology	A	C
Landscape Design	A	C
Landscape Technology	A	C
Nursery Technology	A	C
Sustainable Urban Landscapes	A	C
Paralegal Studies	A	
Real Estate	A	C
Broker's License		C
Surveying	A	C
Water/Wastewater Technology		
Backflow and Cross Connection Control	A	C
Water Distribution Systems Operations	A	C
Water Resources Management	A	C
Water Treatment Plant Operator	A	C
Wastewater Collection Systems	A	C
Wastewater Treatment Operator	A	C

A—Associate Degree Program C—Certificate Program

CYPRESS COLLEGE

9200 Valley View St
Cypress CA 90630-5897
714-484-7000
www.cypresscollege.edu

Dr. Steve Donley, Dean, Career Technical Education and Economic Development

Enrollment: Full-time 4,600 Part-time 9,200

Semester System; Short term classes; Summer intersessions; Winter intersessions

No Housing

OCCUPATIONAL PROGRAMS

Program	A	C
Accounting	A	C
Advanced Airline Customer Service	A	C
Advanced Flight Attendant	A	C
Advanced Networking		C
Advanced Travel/Tourism	A	C
Advanced Web Page Design		C
Advertising and Illustrative Photography		C
Advertising Design	A	
Aerobic Instructor		C
Air Conditioning and Refrigeration	A	C
Alcohol and Drug Studies		C
Animation 2D Computer Graphics		C
Animation 3D Computer Graphics		C
Applied Photography		
Color Photography		C
Creative Photo Arts		C
Darkroom Technician/Assistant		C
Digital Photo Technician		C
Digital Photography		C
Multimedia Photography		C
Photography	A	C
Aquatic Specialist		C
Athletic Coach		C
Automotive Damage Appraisal		C
Automotive Technology	A	C
Brake and Alignment Specialist		C
Collision Repair	A	C
Insurance Co/Auto Collision Repair Industry Management		C
Electrical Diagnostic Specialist		C
Electrical Systems Specialist		C
Emissions Control Specialist		C
Engine Specialist		C
Maintenance Technician		C
Paint/Refinishing		C
Performance and Driveability		C
Sales and Service		C
Service Advisor		C
Toyota Specialist		C
Toyota Technician		C
Transmission Specialist		C
Aviation		
Certificate I–Private Pilot		C
Certificate II–Instrument Pilot		C
Certificate III–Commercial Pilot		C
Certificate IV–Advanced Pilot		C
Commercial Pilot		C
Commercial Pilot/Professional Pilot	A	C
Management	A	C
Basic Airline Customer Service		C
Basic Baker		C
Basic Cook		C
Basic Cruise Line Sales & Operations		C
Basic Flight Attendant		C
Basic Tourism and Conference Management		C
Basic Travel Tourism		C
Business		
Administration	A	
Economics		C
Management	A	C
CISCO Networking		C
Commercial Music Management		C
Computer		
Applications	A	C
Forensics		C
Graphics		C
Information Systems	A	C
Multimedia Art		C
Programming	A	C
Vector Illustration		C
Conflict Resolution		C
Costume/Makeup Design		C
Court Reporting	A	C
Communication Access Realtime Translation (CART)		C
Computer Editor (Scopist)		
Court and Agency Services		C
Text Entry Specialist: Business		C
Text Entry Specialist: Medical		C
Criminal Justice		C
Culinary Arts	A	C
Dining Room Operations		C

A—Associate Degree Program C—Certificate Program

CYPRESS COLLEGE (continued)

Program	A	C
Dance Choreography		C
Dance Teaching		C
Dental Assistant	A	C
Dental Hygiene	A	C
Diagnostic Medical Sonography	A	C
Digital Cinema Arts and Industry		C
Digital Cinema Production		C
Drafting Engineering Tech	A	
Electronic Publishing Design		C
Food Service Management	A	C
Game Programming		C
Geographic Information Systems		C
Health Information Coding		C
Health Information Technology	A	C
Homeland Transportation Security		C
Hotel Management	A	C
Hotel Operations	A	C
Human Services	A	C
Family Studies		C
Victimology		C
Insurance Co/Auto Collision Repair Industry Management (under 'Automotive Collision Repair')		C
Legal Administrative Assistant	A	C
Lighting/Audio design		C
Marine Service Technician		C
Marketing	A	C
Medical		
Insurance Billing Specialist		C
Quality Review Assistant	A	C
Record Clerk		C
Staff Services Science	A	C
Merchandising	A	C
Microsoft Networking		C
Mortuary Science	A	
Motorcycle Technician		C
Multimedia Art		C
Network Hardware Support		C
Network Security		C
Network Systems Administrator		C
Network Systems Engineer		C
Office Technology		
Administrative Assistant	A	C
Administrative Support	A	C
Certificated Professional Secretary		C
Legal Secretary/Administrative Assistant	A	C
Word Processing	A	C
PC/Network Hardware Support		C
Paraprofessional in Education	A	C
Portrait and Wedding Photography		C
Psychiatric Technology	A	C
Radiologic Technology	A	C
Recording Arts		C
Renewable Energy–Wind Turbine Technician		C
Registered Nursing	A	
Restaurant/Lodging Entrepreneur		C
Retail Management (WAFC)	A	C
Room Operations		C
Small Business Management	A	C
Special Event Management		C
Technical Theater		C
Travel/Tourism	A	C
Ultrasound Medical/Sonography		C
Web Networking Technology		C
Web Page Design		C

A—Associate Degree Program C—Certificate Program

DE ANZA COLLEGE

21250 Stevens Creek Blvd
Cupertino CA 95014-5793
408-864-5678
www.deanza.edu

Christina G. Espinosa-Pieb, Vice President of Instruction

Enrollment: Full-time 21,147 Part-time 41,123

Quarter system; 6-8 week summer session

No Housing

OCCUPATIONAL PROGRAMS

Program		
Accounting		C
Bookkeeping		C
Practice Emphasis	A	C
Taxation Emphasis	A	C
Tax Practitioner		C
Administration of Justice		
Corrections/Probation	A	
Law Enforcement	A	
Private Security	A	C
Art–Film/TV: Animation	A	
Automotive Technology (Day)		
Auto Chassis & Powertrain	A	C
Auto Engine Performance	A	C
Auto Machining and Engine Repair	A	C
Automotive Technology (Evening)		
Advanced Automotive		C
Advanced Engine Performance	A	C
Auto Chassis	A	C
Auto Machining and Engine Repair	A	C
Auto Powertrain	A	C
Basic Engine Performance		C
Intermediate Engine Performance		C
Smog Technician		C
Business Administration	A	C
Entrepreneurship		C
Management	A	C
Marketing Management	A	C
Business Software Applications	A	C
Child Development	A	C
Early Childhood Mental Health		C
Early Intervention/Special Ed Assistant		C
Computer Aided Design (CAD)–Mechanical	A	C
Creo Parametric		C
Solid Works		C
Computer Information Systems		
Business Programming	A	C
Enterprise Security Professional	A	C
Database Design for Developers		C
Network Administration	A	C
Network Basics		C
Network Programming	A	C
Programming in C/C++		C
Programming in JAVA		C
Programming in Perl		C
Systems Programming	A	C
UNIX/LINUX Operating System		C
Visual Basic Programming		C
Web Development		C
Environmental Studies		
Energy Management and Building Science	A	C
Environmental Resource Management		
Pollution Prevention	A	C
Wildlife Science Technician		C
Film/TV	A	C
Animation	A	
Production	A	C
Screenwriting	A	
Graphic and Interactive Design	A	C
Health Technologies		
Business Office Clerk		C
Insurance Coding		C
Lab Assisting		C
Medical Assisting	A	C
Medical File Clerk		C
Medical Reception		C
Medical Records Clerk		C
Medical Secretary		C
Medical Transcription		C
Phlebotomy Technician I		C
Journalism and Mass Communication	A	C
Kinesiology	A	C
Management	A	C
Manufacturing and CNC Technology		
CNC Machinist		C
Massage Therapy	A	C
Medical Laboratory Technology (MLT)	A	C
Nursing		
Registered Nurse (RN)	A	
Paralegal Studies	A	C
Photographic Arts	A	
Professional Photography	A	C
Project Management Practitioner		C
Real Estate	A	C

A—Associate Degree Program C—Certificate Program

COLLEGE OF THE DESERT

43500 Monterey Ave
Palm Desert CA 92260-2499
760-773-2571
760-776-7229 Fax
www.collegeofthedesert.edu

John A. Jaramillo, Dean Applied Sciences and Business,

Enrollment: Full-time 4,090 Part-time 8,053

Semester system; 1 summer session;
Summer-Spring-Fall and short term open entry classes

No Housing

OCCUPATIONAL PROGRAMS

Administration of Justice	A	C
Advanced Transportation Technologies	A	C
Agriculture		
Agri-Business	A	
Agriculture, General	A	
Environmental Horticulture	A	C
Arborist Technician		C
Landscape and Irrigation Technician		C
Pest Management Technician		C
Natural Resources	A	
Desert Naturalist		C
Field Ranger		C
Plant Science	A	
Turfgrass Management	A	C
Technician		C
Air Conditioning/HVACR	A	C
Alcohol and Drug Studies	A	C
Architecture/Environmental Design		
Architectural Technology	A	C
Building Inspection Technology		C
Construction Management	A	C
Real Estate Development		C
Automotive Technology	A	
Air Conditioning		C
Alternate Fuels		C
Electrical		C
Emissions		C
Engine Management		C
General Automotive Service		C
Steering, Suspension and Alignment		C
Transmission and Axle		C
Business and Hospitality Industries		
Accounting	A	C
Administrative Office Assistant		C
Administrative Office Professional		C
Business, General	A	
Computer Information Systems	A	C
Golf Management	A	C
Human Resources Generalist		C
Retail Management		C
Culinary Arts		
Basic Culinary Arts		C
Culinary Management	A	C
Intermediate Culinary Arts		C
Digital Design and Production	A	C
Drafting/CAD	A	C
Early Childhood Education (ECE)	A	
Associate Teacher		C
Early Childhood Education	A	
Master Teacher		C
Teacher		C
Emergency Medical Care		C
Fire Technology	A	C
Health Sciences		
Home Health Aide		C
Nursing Assistant		C
Registered Nursing (ADN)	A	
Vocational Nursing (VN)	A	C
Physical Education/Athletics		
Fitness Specialist		C
Police Science	A	
Reserve Police Officer		C

A—Associate Degree Program C—Certificate Program

DIABLO VALLEY COLLEGE

321 Golf Club Rd
Pleasant Hill CA 94523-1576
925-685-1230
925-685-1551 Fax
www.dvc.edu

Semester system (Flexible calendar)
6 week summer sessions

Rachel Westlake, Vice President, Instruction

Enrollment: Full-time 7,230 Part-time 13,539

No Housing

OCCUPATIONAL PROGRAMS

Addiction Studies		
Addiction Counseling	A	C
Addiction Studies	A	C
Administration of Justice	A	C
Community Relations Specialist		C
Correctional Specialist		C
Crime Scene Investigator		C
Criminal Law Specialist		C
Juvenile Counseling		C
Patrol Specialist		C
Architecture Technology	A	C
Architecture Design	A	C
Art		
Printmaking		C
Art Digital Media		
3D Modeling and Animation		C
Art Digital Media	A	
Character Animation		C
Digital Audio		C
Digital Imaging		C
Graphic Design	A	C
Motion Graphics		C
Web Design		C
Broadcast Communication Arts	A	C
Business	A	C
Advance General Business		C
Accounting	A	C
Bookkeeping		C
Essentials		C
General		C
Management and Leadership Studies		C
Marketing		C
Real Estate		C
Small Business Management/Entrepreneurship		C
Wealth Management		C
Computer Information Systems (CIS)	A	C
Core		C
Database Management	A	C
Project Management	A	C
Web Graphics	A	C
Web Technology	A	C

Computer Network Technology		
Microsoft Windows System Administration	A	
Computer Science-COMSCA		
Advanced C++ Programming		C
Advanced Java Programming		C
Computer Architecture		C
Computer User Support		C
Mobile and Enterprise Java Programming		C
Program Design		C
Computer Studies		
Computer Information Systems (CIS)	A	C
Computer Science	A	C
Computer Technical Support	A	C
Construction		
Building Inspection	A	C
Management	A	C
Supervision and Superintendency	A	C
Culinary Arts		
Baking and Pastry	A	C
Culinary Arts	A	C
Restaurant Management	A	C
Dance	A	
Dental		
Assisting	A	C
Hygiene	A	C
Laboratory Technology	A	C
Early Childhood Education		
Associate Teacher		C
Basic	A	C
Master Teacher		C
Site Supervisor		C
Teacher		C
Electrical/Electronics Technology		C
Energy Systems	A	C
Photovoltaic	A	C
Solar Thermal	A	C
Engineering		
Civil Design Drafting Technology		C
Civil Drafting with CAD		C
Computer Aided Drafting and Digital Media for Engineering and Architecture		C

A—Associate Degree Program C—Certificate Program

DIABLO VALLEY COLLEGE continued

Electrical Engineering and Computer Engineering		C
Industrial Maintenance Machinist/Mechanic	A	C
Mechanical Engineering		C
Geographic Information System/Global Positioning System	A	C
Meterology	A	
Heating, Ventilating, Air Conditioning, Refrigeration-HVACR	A	C
Horticulture		
Arboriculture		C
Landscape Construction and Management		C
Landscape Architecture and Design		C
Retail Nursery		C
Industrial Maintenance Machinist/Mechanic (in TECH)	A	C
Kinesiology		
Coaching	A	C
Fitness Instruction	A	
Group Exercise Instruction		C
Personal Training		C
Specializations	A	
Sports and Recreation Management	A	
Music Industry Studies	A	C
Plumbing	A	C
Respiratory Therapy	A	
Special Education Paraeducator/Instructional Assistant	A	C
Steamfitting	A	C

EAST LOS ANGELES COLLEGE

1301 Avenida Cesar Chavez
Monterey Park CA 91754-6099
323-265-8973
323-265-8635 Fax
www.elac.edu

Semester system; 5 week summer sessions

Renee D. Martinez, Vice President, Workforce Education and Economic Development
Gayle Brosseau, Dean, Economic Development
Laura M. Ramirez, Dean, Vocational Education

Enrollment: Full-time 28,000 Part-time 11,239

No Housing

OCCUPATIONAL PROGRAMS

Administration of Justice	A	C
Basic Police Academy Preparation		C
Forensic Crime Scene Investigation		C
Law Emphasis		C
Sociological Emphasis		C
Administrative Assistant		C
Animation	A	
Animation Levels 1,2		C
Architectural		
Computer-Aided Design	A	C
Design		C
Drafting	A	C
Drawing		C
Art Graphic Communication	A	C
Automotive Technology	A	C
Cooling Systems and Climate Control Specialist		C
Drivetrain Specialist		C
Engine Performance and Driveability		C
Biological Applications of Electron Microscopy		C
Business Administration		
Accounting	A	C
Business Management	A	C
Chemical Dependency Counselor		C
Chemical Dependency Specialist in Criminal Justice		C
Child Development	A	
Infant/Toddler Emphasis		C
Site Supervisor–Certificate 3		C
Teacher–Certificate 2		C
Clerical Assistant		C
Color Printing and Processing		C
Computer Science Information Technology	A	
Microcomputers		C
Programming		C
Customer Service Representative		C
Desktop Publishing	A	C
Digital Imaging		C
Elder Care/Gerontology		C
Electron Microscopy Technician	A	C
Engineering Graphics		C
Engineering Graphics and Design Technology	A	C
Executive Assistant	A	C
Fire Technology	A	
State Fire Marshal Core Classes		C
Health Information		
Clerk Typist		C
Coding and Statistics Clerk		C
Coding Specialist		C
Technology	A	C
Histotechnologist		C
Internet Specialist		C
Journalism	A	C
Kinesiology		
Physical Education	A	
Large Format Photography		C
Legal Secretary	A	C
Marketing	A	C
Medical Assisting	A	C
Multimedia (Level 1, 2)	A	C
Music	A	
Nursing (LVN to RN)	A	C
Nursing, Registered (RN)	A	
Office Assistant		C
Office Systems Specialist	A	C
Photography	A	
Photography and Digital Imaging		C
Real Estate	A	C
Real Estate Broker		C
Registered Nurse Curriculum for Licensed Vocational Nurse, 30 Unit Option		C
Respiratory Therapy	A	C
Respiratory Therapy, Non-traditional	A	
Stage Management and Production		C
Studio Lighting and Techniques		C
Teacher-Certificate 2		
Technology and Logistics	A	C
Theater Arts	A	
Transcriber		C
Word information Processor		C

A—Associate Degree Program C—Certificate Program

EL CAMINO COLLEGE

16007 Crenshaw Blvd
Torrance CA 90506-0001
310-532-3670
www.elcamino.edu

Semester system; Mid-semester courses (9 weeks)
6 and 8 week summer sessions

Stephanie Rodriquez, Dean, Industry and Technology

Enrollment: Full-time 5,954 Part-time 16,662

No Housing

OCCUPATIONAL PROGRAMS

Administration of Justice	A	C
Forensics		C
Air Conditioning and Refrigeration	A	C
Electrical Controls		C
Heating, Ventilating, and Air Conditioning (HVAC)		C
Architecture	A	C
Art		
Gallery Management		C
Jewelry Design and Fabrication		C
Automotive Technology	A	C
Accident Reconstruction		C
Air Conditioning Technician		C
Automotive Collision Repair/Painting, I and II		C
Brake/Suspension Technician		C
Collision Investigation		C
Engine Rebuilding/Repair Technician		C
Technician I and II		C
Transmission/Drive Train Technician		C
Tune-Up Technician		C
Business		
Accounting	A	C
Administration	A	
Management	A	
Child Development		
Early Childhood Education		C
Early Intervention Assistant		C
Special Education Assistant		C
Computer Aided Design/Drafting	A	C
Auto Cad Mechanical Drafting Technician		C
Computer Information Systems	A	C
Microcomputer Applications		C
Microcomputer Support and Network Management		C
Computer Science	A	C
Construction Technology	A	C
Cabinet and Fine Woodworking	A	C
Cosmetology	A	C
Level I		C
Dance	A	
Digital Arts		
Computer Animation		C
Digital Photography		C
Illustration		C
Motion Graphics		C
Web Design		C
Electronics and Computer Hardware Technology		
CompTIA Computer Hardware Technician		C
Computer Hardware Electronics Technician		C
Computer Hardware Technician	A	C
Electronics Engineering Technician		C
Electronics Technician		C
Industrial Computer Control Technician		C
Power Electronics Certificate A		C
Robotics		C
Engineering Technology/Technician	A	C
Environmental Horticultural Science	A	C
Fashion		
Computer Patternmaking Technician		C
Costume Technician		C
Design & Production	A	C
Merchandising	A	C
Stylist		C
Film/Video Production	A	C
Fire and Emergency Technology	A	C
Fire Academy		C
Paramedical Technician	A	C
Industrial Technology	A	
Journalism	A	C
Machine Tool Technology		
CNC Machine Operator		C
Machinist	A	C
Numerical Control Programmer	A	C
Manufacturing Technology	A	C
Marketing	A	C
Music–Commercial		C
Nursing	A	
Office Administration		
Bookkeeping Clerk		C
Management	A	
Office Applications Specialist		C
Office Systems	A	C
Paralegal Studies	A	C
Photography	A	C

A—Associate Degree Program C—Certificate Program

EL CAMINO COLLEGE continued

Physical Education	A	
Radiologic Technology	A	C
Real Estate		
Appraisal	A	C
Mortgage Loan Brokerage	A	C
Recreation	A	
Respiratory Care	A	C
Retail Management		C
Sign Language/Interpreter Training	A	C
Theatre	A	
Entertainment Lighting Technology		C
Visual Communications		C
Welding	A	C

A—Associate Degree Program C—Certificate Program

EVERGREEN VALLEY COLLEGE

3095 Yerba Buena Rd
San Jose CA 95135-1598
408-274-7900
408-223-9291 Fax
www.evc.edu

Lena Tran, Dean, Business and Workforce Development

Enrollment: Full-time 2,138 Part-time 10,100

Semester system; Many irregularly scheduled classes

No Housing

OCCUPATIONAL PROGRAMS

Accounting	A	C
Administration of Justice	A	
Art & Design		
Design Emphasis	A	
Automotive Technology		
Advanced Automotive Training		C
American Honda Program		C
Basic Skills–Entry Level Employment		C
Drivetrain and Chassis	A	C
Electrical-Engine Performance	A	C
Smog Specialist		C
Building Information Modeling (BIM)		C
Business Administration	A	
Computer Aided Design and Drafting	A	
3D CADD		C
Architectural CADD		C
AutoDesk		C
Digital Prototyping		C
Mechanical Modeling		C
Engineering	A	
Entrepreneurship		C
General Business	A	C
Information Processing Specialist	A	C
Law Enforcement (Police Academy)		C
Medical Assistant-Front Office		C
Nursing	A	
Paralegal Studies	A	C
Surveying and Geomatics	A	C

A—Associate Degree Program C—Certificate Program

FEATHER RIVER COLLEGE

570 Golden Eagle Ave.
Quincy CA 95971-6023
530-283-0202
530-283-3757 Fax
www.frc.edu

Semester system; 6 and 9 week summer sessions

Derek Lerch, Dean of Instruction/CIO

Enrollment: Full-time 600 Part-time 2,000

Student housing is available

OCCUPATIONAL PROGRAMS

Accounting (BUS)		C
Accounting Management (BUS)		C
Associate Teacher (ECE)		C
Administration of ECE Programs (ECE)		C
Administration of Justice	A	C
Athletic Training (HES)		C
Backcountry Search and Rescue (ORL)		C
Baking Entrepreneurship (NCA)		C
Biological Science Technician (ENVR)		C
Business (BUS)	A	C
Business Management (BUS)		C
Catering Entrepreneurship (NCA)		C
Child Care Entrepreneurship (ECE)		C
Child Development/Early Childhood Education	A	C
Culinary Arts (NCA)	A	C
Early Childhood Education (ECE)	A	C
Elementary Teacher Preparation (ECE)	A	
Entrepreneurial Planning (BUS)		C
Environmental Studies (ENVR)	A	C
Equine Studies (AG)	A	C
Finance (BUS)		C
Fisheries (ENVR)		C
Forestry Technician (ENVR)		C
Fundamentals of Ranch Skills (AG)		C
General Agriculture (AG)		C
General Business (BUS)		C
Hatchery Technician (ENVR)		C
Health and Exercise Studies (HES)	A	C
Horse Training Skills (AG)		C
Hydrologic Technician (ENVR)		C
Infant/Toddler (ECE)		C
Kinesiology (HES)	A	
Licensed Vocational Nursing (NURS)	A	
Management (BUS)		C
Marketing (BUS)		C
Master Teacher - Creative Curriculum (ECE)		C
Master Teacher - Special Needs (ECE)		C
Multimedia (ICT)	A	C
Mobile Application Development (ECT)		C
Nutrition, Foods, and Culinary Arts (NCA)	A	
Office Technology (ICT)	A	C
Outdoor Recreation Leadership (ORL)	A	C
ORL Entrepreneurship (ORL)		C
Pack Station & Stable Operation (AG)	A	C
Range Technology (AG)		C
Restaurant Management (NCA)		C
Rodeo Techniques (AG)		C
Small Business (BUS)		C
Small Business Management (BUS)		C
Teacher (ECE)		C
Teaching/Coaching (HES)		C
Vocational Nursing (LVN)	A	C
Water Resources Technician (ENVR)		C
Web Development (ICT)	A	C
Wildlife Technician (ENVR)		C

A—Associate Degree Program C—Certificate Program

FOLSOM LAKE COLLEGE

10 College Parkway
Folsom CA 95630
916-608-6500
www.flc.losrios.edu

Gary Hartley, Dean of Instruction and Technology

Enrollment: Full-time & Part-time 9,000

Semester system, 6 & 9 week summer session

No Housing

OCCUPATIONAL PROGRAMS

Accounting	A	
Accounting–Advanced		C
Accounting Clerk		C
Accounting–Computer Applications		C
Administration of Justice	A	
Business		
Administration	A	
Administrative Assistant	A	
Business: General	A	
Office Assistant		C
Office Technician		C
Small Business Management/ Entrepreneurship	A	C
Communication Studies	A	
Applied Communication Skills		C
Computer Information Science (CIS)	A	
Computer Programmer SQL		C
Computer Programming	A	
Computer Science	A	
Database Analyst SQL		C
Programming		C
Rational Database Administration		C
Early Childhood Education	A	
Assistant Teacher		C
Associate Teacher		C
Family Child Care		C
Infant Specialist		C
Master Teacher		C
School Age Specialist		C
Site Supervisor	A	C
Teacher		C
Environmental Technology		
Water Management		C
Fire Technology	A	C
Geology	A	
Human Services	A	C
General	A	C
Gerontology	A	C
Home Caregiver		C
Management	A	
Purchasing		C
Marketing	A	
Medical Technology		
Medical Laboratory Technician	A	
Project Management		C
Real Estate	A	
Broker		C
Sales		C

A—Associate Degree Program C—Certificate Program

FOOTHILL COLLEGE

12345 El Monte Rd
Los Altos Hills CA 94022-4599
650-949-7777
650-949-7375 Fax
www.foothill.edu

Quarter system; 6 week summer session

Katie Townsend-Merino, Vice-President of Instruction

Enrollment: Full-time 4,771 Part-time 12,127

No Housing

OCCUPATIONAL PROGRAMS

Accounting	A	C
Bookkeeping Specialist		C
CPA Examination Preparation		C
Enrolled Agent Preparation		C
Financial Accounting		C
Payroll Preparation		C
Tax Accounting		C
Tax Specialist		C
Business Administration	A	
Business International Studies	A	C
Child Development	A	
Child Development Teacher		C
Early Childhood Education		C
Inclusion and Children with Special Needs		C
Infant Toddler Development		C
Program Supervision and Mentoring		C
School-Aged Child Care		C
Dental Assisting	A	C
Dental Hygiene	A	
Diagnostic Medical Sonography	A	
Emergency Medical Technician		C
Enterprise Networking	A	
Cisco Academy CCNA		C
Cisco Academy CCNP		C
Microsoft Windows MCSA		C
VMware		C
Environmental Horticulture and Design	A	C
Geographic Information Systems (GIS)		C
Graphic and Interactive Design	A	C
Book Arts		C
Garment Printing		C
Graphic Design		C
Illustration		C
Motion Graphics		C
Printmaking		C
Printmaking Studio		C
Web Design and Development		C
Kinesiology and Athletics		
Adaptive Fitness Therapy	A	C
Music Technology	A	C
ProTools		C
Nanoscience	A	C
Paramedic	A	C
Pharmacy Technician	A	C
Photography	A	C
Digital Photography		C
Photo Criticism		C
Photographic Lab Technician		C
Traditional Photography		C
Primary Care Associate	A	C
Radiologic Technology	A	
Respiratory Therapy	A	
Theatre Arts	A	C
Actor Training		C
Theatre Technology		C
Theatre Production Organization		C
Veterinary Technology	A	
Veterinary Assisting		C

A—Associate Degree Program C—Certificate Program

FRESNO CITY COLLEGE

1101 E University Ave
Fresno CA 93741-0001
559-442-4600
559-489-2281 Fax
www.fresnocitycollege.edu

Semester system; 4-6-8-10 week summer sessions

Jacob Jackson, Dean of Instruction

Enrollment: Full-time 8,504 Part-time 14,822

No Housing

OCCUPATIONAL PROGRAMS

Account Clerk		C
Accounting	A	C
Business Accounting and Finance		C
Computerized Accounting		C
Full Charge Bookkeeper		C
Junior Accountant		C
Adaptive Ornamental Horticulture Skills		C
Administration of Justice		
Adult Correctional Office Core		C
Basic Police Academy		C
Basic Supervision		C
Juvenile Correctional Officer Core		C
Probation Core		C
Public Safety Dispatchers' Course		C
Requalification-Basic Course		C
Air Conditioning	A	C
Air Conditioning Technology Overview		C
Commercial Air Conditioning, Heating, and Duct Systems		C
Digital Air Conditioning Controls		C
Industrial Refrigeration–CARO/EPA Section 608 Certificate		C
Mechanical and Electrical Systems		C
Architecture	A	C
Automotive Collision Repair Technology	A	C
Automotive Technology	A	C
Chassis Technician		C
Emission Technician		C
General Motors ASEP	A	
Powertrain Technician		C
Building Safety and Code Administration	A	C
Business Administration	A	
Entrepreneurial Ventures		C
Human Relations and Communications		C
Human Resource Management Assistant		C
Management	A	
Logistics and Distribution Management		C
Management and Supervision		C
Personal Finance and Investments		C
Small Business Management		C
Business and Technology		
Business Office Assistant	A	
Clerical Training		C
Computer Applications Software		C
Legal Office Professional	A	C
Medical Office Assistant		C
Medical Office Professional	A	C
Microsoft Word		C
Office Manager		C
Office Professional I	A	C
Office Professional II	A	C
Business Finance and Investments		C
Business Finance and Accounting		C
Child Development	A	C
Associate Teacher		C
Early Intervention Assistant		C
Family Child Care		C
Foster Care		C
CISCO Certification		C
CISCO CCNP Preparation		C
CISCO Firewall Specialist		C
Commercial Music	A	C
Computer Aided Drafting and Design (CADD)	A	C
Computer Aided Manufacturing (CAM)	A	C
Computer Information Technology		
Computer Information Systems	A	
Data Entry Technician		C
Information Security I		C
Information Security II		C
MCSE Core		C
MCSE Networking		C
Microsoft Access		C
Microsoft Excel		C
Microsoft Office		C
Microcomputer Software Specialist	A	C
Networking/Computer Technician	A	C
Preparation in Microsoft Office		C
Systems Support Specialist		C
Web Developer	A	C
Web Page Development		C
Construction	A	C

A—Associate Degree Program C—Certificate Program

FRESNO CITY COLLEGE(continued)

Program		
Criminology		
Correctional Science	A	C
Criminology	A	C
Forensic Evidence	A	C
Law Enforcement	A	C
Pre-Academy Training		C
Culinary Arts		
Advanced Culinary Arts		C
Basic Culinary Arts		C
Intermediate Culinary Arts		C
Dance	A	
Dental Hygiene	A	
Educational Aide, Special Education		C
Electrical Systems Technology	A	C
Automation Control Technician		C
CISCO CCNA Preparation		C
CISCO CCNP Preparation		C
Communications Technology		C
Control Systems		C
Electrical Line/Utility Worker		C
Industrial Controls		C
Networking/Computer Technician	A	C
Network Security		C
Wireless Networks		C
Emergency Medical Technician		C
Emergency Medical Technician Refresher		C
Engineering	A	
Fashion Merchandising		
(Marketing/Home Economics)	A	C
Fire Technology	A	C
Basic Fire Academy		C
Prehospital Paramedic Care		C
Food and Nutrition	A	
Dietary Aide		C
Dietetic Service Supervision		C
Food Service Management		C
Child Nutrition		C
Graphic Communications	A	C
Digital/Video Option		C
Graphic Design Option	A	C
Multimedia Option		C
Web Design		C
Health Information Technology	A	
Medical Coding		C
Home Economics Consumer Education	A	C
Human Services		
Alcoholism and Drug Abuse Counseling	A	C
Social Work Option	A	C
Industrial Arts Technology	A	C
Construction Option	A	C
Manufacturing Option	A	C
Journalism	A	
Library Technology	A	C
Manufacturing Technician		C

Program		
Marketing	A	C
Advertising		C
Fashion Merchandising	A	C
Personal Sales		C
Retailing	A	C
Retail Management	A	C
Medical Assistant - Clinician	A	
Music		
Commercial Music	A	C
Guitar	A	
Instrumental	A	
Piano	A	
Vocal		C
Nursing (RN)	A	
Paralegal	A	C
Professional Photography	A	C
Commercial Photography		C
Digital Photography		C
Photojournalism		C
Radiologic Technology	A	
Real Estate	A	C
Broker/Sales Option	A	C
Escrow Option	A	C
Housing Management Option	A	C
Recreation	A	
Respiratory Care Practitioner	A	
Sign Language Interpreting Preparation		C
Surgical Technology	A	
Teacher Aide	A	C
Theatre Arts		
Design/Technical Theatre Studies	A	
Welding Technology		
Metal Fabrication Option	A	C
Pipe and Structural Steel Certification Option	A	C
Welding Design and Fabrication		C
Welding Multi-Process		C
Wind Turbine Technician		C

A—Associate Degree Program C—Certificate Program

FULLERTON COLLEGE

321 E Chapman Ave
Fullerton CA 92832-2095
714-992-7000
714-447-4097 Fax
www.fullcoll.edu

Semester system; 4 to 6 week summer sessions

Scott McKenzie, Dean of Technology and Engineering

Enrollment: Full-time 5,944 Part-time 14,141

No Housing

OCCUPATIONAL PROGRAMS

Program	A	C
Accounting	A	C
Administration of Justice	A	C
Crime Scene Investigation		C
P.O.S.T. Law Enforcement		C
Advertising	A	C
Advertising and Graphic Design		C
Architectural	A	
Architectural CAD Technology		C
Art Computer Graphics		C
3D Animation Certificate—Level II		C
Computer Animation/Multimedia		C
Desktop Publishing		C
Automotive		
Automatic Transmission Specialist		C
Automotive Chassis Specialist		C
Automotive Maintenance Specialist		C
Automotive Management		C
Automotive Service Advisor		C
Automotive Technology	A	C
Emission Control Specialist		C
Engine Performance Specialist		C
Fabrication Specialist		C
Light Repair Specialist		C
Manual Drive Train Specialist		C
Biological Technician	A	
Business Administration	A	
Business and Technology Skills		C
Business Management	A	C
E-Business Development		C
Entrepreneurship	A	C
International Business Management	A	C
International Business Skills		C
Managerial Communications		C
Project Management		C
Carpentry	A	
Child Development and Educational Studies	A	
Early Childhood Education Administration		C
Early Childhood Education Associate Teacher		C
Family Child Care		C
Infant/Toddler Caregiver		C
School Age		C
Weekend Associate Teacher		C
Civil Engineering Technology	A	
Communications—General	A	
Radio and Television/Video Production		C
Radio Broadcasting	A	C
Radio Production	A	
Sports Broadcasting		C
Television/Film Production	A	
Computer Information Systems	A	C
Computer Software Application Specialist		C
Database Applications		C
E-Commerce Programming		C
Enterprise Database		C
Internet		C
Networking		C
PC Applications		C
Programming		C
Spreadsheet Applications		C
Web Design		C
Web Scripting		C
Construction		
Estimating		C
Inspection	A	C
Management	A	
Technology	A	C
Cosmetology	A	C
Esthetician		C
Instructor	A	
Early Childhood Education	A	
Engineering	A	
Environmental Technology	A	C
Fashion Design	A	C
Advanced Fashion Design		C
Dressmaking–Alterations		C
Fashion Illustration		C
Fashion Journalism	A	
Fashion Merchandising	A	C
Image Consultant		C
Patternmaker		C
Product Development Apparel		C
Textiles and Clothing	A	
Foods and Nutrition	A	

A—Associate Degree Program C—Certificate Program

FULLERTON COLLEGE (continued)

Program	A	C
Horticulture		
Greenhouse and Nursery Production		C
Landscape Design/Management		C
Landscape Irrigation		C
Landscape Management	A	C
Nursery Management	A	
Ornamental Horticulture	A	C
Pest Management		C
Industrial Arts	A	
Industrial Laboratory Technician (Chemistry)	A	
Industrial Drafting	A	
Level I		C
Level II		C
Industrial Technology	A	
Interior Design Assistant	A	
Interior Design Commercial Design		C
Interior Merchandising		C
Residential Design		C
Journalism	A	C
Machine Technology		C
CNC Operator		C
Computer Numerical Control (CNC)		C
Machine Technology Level I		C
Machine Technology Level II		C
Manufacturing Technology	A	
Mastercam		C
Surfcam		C
Marketing Management	A	C
Medical Technology	A	
Music		
Commercial	A	
Piano Teaching		C
Recording/Production		C
Office Technology		
Administrative Office Assistant	A	C
Legal Office Administration	A	C
Word Processing	A	C
Paralegal Studies	A	C
Photography	A	
Professional Photography		C
Physical Education	A	
Aquatic Specialist		C
Athletic Coach		C
Group Fitness Instructor		C
Personal Trainer		C
Physical Education—Fitness	A	
Therapeutic and Sports Massage		
Level I Therapist		C
Printing Technology	A	C
Advanced Offset Presswork		C
Customer Service Training		C
Digital Printing		C
Electronic Imaging		C
Flexography		C
Graphic Communications		C
Offset Duplicator Training		C
Printing Technology (General)		C
Quick Print/In-Plant Graphics		C
Screen Printing		C
Public Relations		C
Real Estate Management	A	C
Real Estate Sales		C
Theatre Arts (Drama)	A	
Assistant Costume Designer		C
Costume Cutter/Draper		C
Costume Stitcher		C
Costume Wardrobe		C
Lighting Technician		C
Musical Theatre		C
Musical Theatre (Advanced)		C
Scenic Artist		C
Sound Technician		C
Stage Management		C
Technical Theatre		C
Theatrical Costumer		C
Theatrical Costumer (Advanced)		C
Welding Technology		C

A—Associate Degree Program C—Certificate Program

GAVILAN COLLEGE

5055 Santa Teresa Blvd
Gilroy CA 95020-9599
408-848-4800
408-848-4801 Fax
www.gavilan.edu

Semester system; 6 week summer session; 3 week winter session

Sherrean Carr, Dean of Career Technical Education

Enrollment: Full-time 1,441 Part-time 5,094

No Housing

OCCUPATIONAL PROGRAMS

Administration of Justice		
Corrections	A	C
Law Enforcement	A	C
Allied Health: Nursing: Registered Nursing, LVN, CNA, HHA, MA	A	C
Aviation Maintenance Technology		
Airframe	A	C
Powerplant	A	C
Biotechnology		C
Business		
Accounting	A	C
Computer Applications		C
Computerized Accounting		C
Economics	A	C
General Business	A	C
General Office Skills	A	C
Medical Office	A	C
Real Estate	A	C
Retail Management	A	C
Child Development	A	
Early Childhood Education	A	C
Early Intervention Assistant		C
Family Child Care		C
School Age Child Care		C
Spanish Early Childhood Education		C
Computer Graphics and Design		
Advanced Technical Computer Graphics	A	C
Computer Graphics for Environmental Design	A	C
Technical Desktop Publishing and Graphics	A	C
Computer Science and Information Systems		
Business Computer Applications	A	C
Hardware		C
Networking	A	C
Programming	A	C
Programming for the Internet	A	C
Scientific Programming	A	C
UNIX Operating System	A	C
Cosmetology	A	C
Esthetician		C
Digital Media		
Digital Art and Imaging	A	C
Digital Audio/Video	A	C
Digital Imaging/Graphics Production		C
Digital Print Production		C
Digital Video Editor Specialist		C
Interactive Media and Authoring	A	C
Web Page Production Specialist		C
Water Resource Management	A	C

A—Associate Degree Program C—Certificate Program

GLENDALE COMMUNITY COLLEGE

1500 N Verdugo Rd
Glendale CA 91208-2894
818-240-1000
818-549-9436 Fax
www.glendale.edu

Semester system; winter intersession and 2 summer sessions

Jan Swinton, Associate Dean, Instructional Services & Workforce Development

Enrollment: Full-time 5,279 Part-time 10,290

No Housing

OCCUPATIONAL PROGRAMS

Program		
Accounting	A	C
Administration of Justice	A	C
Alcohol/ Drug Studies Specialist	A	C
Animation		
Classical Animation	A	C
Digital Animation	A	C
Architecture Drafting and Design	A	C
Aviation and Transportation		
Aviation Administration	A	C
Flight Attendant		C
Pilot Training	A	C
Bookkeeping	A	C
Business Administration	A	
Entrepreneurship/Small Business	A	C
Financial Planning and Investment	A	C
General Business	A	C
International Business	A	C
Child Development		
Infant/Toddler	A	C
Master Teacher	A	C
School-Age Care	A	C
Site Supervisor	A	C
Teacher–Preschool	A	C
Computer Applications and Business Office Technologies		
Administrative Assistant	A	C
General Office	A	C
Legal Secretary	A	C
Computer Applications Specialist		C
Computer Applications Technician		C
Computer Information Systems		C
Computer Numerical Control Technician	A	C
Computer Programmer		C
Computer Science	A	C
Computer Software Technician	A	C
Computer Support Technician		C
Computerized Accounting Specialist		C
Culinary Nutrition, and Hospitality Management	A	
Dietary Service Supervisor	A	C
Restaurant Management	A	C
Dance Teaching	A	C
Dental Front Office/Billing and Coding		C
Desktop Publishing Technician		C
Electro/Mechanical Fabrication Technician		C
Electronics and Computer Technology		
Electronics Engineering Technician	A	C
Emergency Medical Technician		C
Engineering/Electro-Mechanical Design		
Electro/Mechanical Design	A	C
Fire Technology	A	C
Insurance Professional		C
Insurance Specialist	A	C
Life and Health	A	C
Property and Casualty	A	C
Machine and Manufacturing Technology		
Machine Technology		C
Machinist	A	C
Management	A	C
Marketing	A	C
Mass Communications	A	C
Medical Office Administration		
Medical Billing and Coding		C
Medical Front Office	A	C
Medical Secretary	A	C
Medical Transcription	A	C
Nursing		
30 Unit Option		C
Generic Associate Degree Nursing	A	
Career Ladder	A	C
Registered Nursing	A	
Photography	A	C
Real Estate	A	C
Real Estate Appraisal	A	C
Receptionist/Office Clerk		C
Retail Management		C
Tax Preparer		C
Technical Theatre	A	C
Television Production		
Corporate Television Option	A	C
Mass Media Option	A	C
Videography Option	A	C
Theater Arts	A	

A—Associate Degree Program C—Certificate Program

GLENDALE COMMUNITY COLLEGE (continued)

Unix System Administrator		C
Visual Arts	A	
Web Development	A	C
Welding, Occupational (Combination Welder)	A	C

A—Associate Degree Program C—Certificate Program

GOLDEN WEST COLLEGE

15744 Golden West St
P O Box 2748
Huntington Beach CA 92647-2748
714-892-7711
714-895-8164 Fax
www.goldenwestcollege.edu

16 week semester system; 6 & 4 week summer sessions

Omid Pourzanjani, Dean, Career & Techanical Education

Enrollment: Full-time 5,140 Part-time 8,133

No Housing

OCCUPATIONAL PROGRAMS

Accounting		
Accounting	A	
Enrolled Agent Tax Specialist		C
Staff Accountant		C
American Sign Language Interpreting	A	
Automotive Technology		
Chassis and Drivetrain Specialist	A	C
Engine Performance & Emission Specialist	A	C
Business Administration	A	
Computer Aided Design and Drafting CADD		C
Computer Business Applications	A	C
Administrative Assistant	A	C
Certified Basic Professional: CPS/CAP	A	C
Legal Secretary/Assistant	A	C
Microsoft Office		C
Computer Science		
Software Development		C
Video Game Development		C
Cosmetology		
Cosmetology	A	C
Esthetician	A	C
Criminal Justice Training Center	A	
Administration of Justice	A	
Law Enforcement	A	C
Police Academy	A	
Special Investigator		C
Design		C
Digital Arts		
Biotechnology Media Design		C
Graphic Design Advanced Production		C
Graphic Design and Production		C
Graphic Design Foundation		C
Graphic Design Web Site Design		C
Digital Media	A	C
Audio Recording		C
Video Production		C
Early Childhood Education	A	
Environmental Studies		
Energy Efficiency and Renewable Energy	A	
Recycling and Resource Management		C
Floral Design and Shop Management	A	C
Journalism	A	
Kinesiology	A	
Management		
General Management		C
Human Resources Management		C
Management	A	C
Marketing	A	C
Retail Management		C
Retail Management and Entrepreneurship	A	
Small Business Management		C
Theatre Arts	A	

A—Associate Degree Program C—Certificate Program

GROSSMONT COLLEGE

8800 Grossmont College Dr
El Cajon CA 92020-1799
619-644-7000
619-644-7922 Fax
www.grossmont.edu

Jim Custeau, Interim Dean, Career Technical Education /Workforce Development

Enrollment: Full-time 6,000 Part-time 10,000

Semester system; 6 and 8 week summer session

No Housing

OCCUPATIONAL PROGRAMS

Administration of Justice		
Corrections	A	C
Forensic Technology	A	C
Law Enforcement	A	C
Legal Systems and Court Management	A	C
Security Academy		C
Security Management	A	C
American Sign Language	A	C
Art		
Digital Media	A	
Drawing and Painting	A	
Photography	A	
Business Administration	A	C
Business-General	A	C
Insurance Services		C
Business Office Technology		
Account Clerk		C
Administrative Assistant	A	C
Executive Assistant	A	
Front Office/Receptionist		C
Medical Office Assistant		C
Office Assistant, Level I		C
Office Assistant, Level II		C
Office Professional		C
Office Software Specialist, Level I		C
Office Software Specialist, Level II		C
Virtual Office Assistant		C
Cardiovascular Technology		
Adult Echocardiography	A	
Telemetry/ECG Technician		C
Vascular Technology	A	C
Child Development	A	C
Associate Teacher		C
Master Teacher	A	C
Site Supervisor	A	C
Computer Science Information Systems		
Computer Programming	A	C
Local Area Network (LAN) Support Specialist	A	C
Small Computer Specialist	A	C
Web Design	A	C
Culinary Arts		C
Baking and Pastry	A	C
Banquet Cook		C
Culinary Entrepreneurship	A	C
Line Cook		C
Pastry Cook		C
Prep Cook		C
Dance	A	C
Disability Services Management	A	C
Exercise Science and Wellness	A	C
Athletic Training	A	C
Fitness Specialist		C
Geology	A	
Hospitality and Tourism Management	A	C
International Business	A	C
Management	A	C
Marketing	A	C
Media Communications		
Audio Production	A	C
Cross-Media Journalism	A	C
Video Production	A	C
Multimedia		
Software Development	A	C
Video	A	C
Visual Design	A	C
Web Authoring	A	C
Nursing		
Registered Nursing Program	A	
Occupational Therapy Assistant	A	
Oceanography	A	
Orthopedic Technology	A	C
Respiratory Therapy	A	C
Retail Management	A	C
Theatre Arts		
Acting	A	C
Technical	A	C
Tribal Gaming: Culture and Policies		C

A—Associate Degree Program C—Certificate Program

HARTNELL COLLEGE

156 Homestead Ave
Salinas CA 93901-1697
831-755-6960
831-759-6045 Fax
www.hartnell.edu

Semester system, 6 & 8 week summer session

Zahi Atallah, Dean of Academic Affairs

Enrollment: Full-time 2,188 Part-time 6,164

No Housing

OCCUPATIONAL PROGRAMS

Administration of Justice	A	C
Agriculture		
Business Emphasis	A	C
Food Safety		C
Production Emphasis	A	C
Alcohol and Drug Abuse Counseling	A	C
Auto Technology		
Automotive Shop Management	A	C
General Automotive Mechanics	A	C
Heavy Duty Diesel Technology—Transportation	A	C
Business Administration	A	
Business Office Technology	A	
Computer Science and Information Systems		
Computer Science Option	A	C
Digital and Web Design Option	A	C
Network and Security	A	C
Digital Arts	A	C
Drafting and Design Engineering Technology	A	
Early Childhood Education	A	C
Engineering	A	
Industrial Technology		
Industrial Mechanics		C
Industrial Technician		C
Nursing		
RN	A	
Vocational		C
Photography	A	C
Respiratory Care Practitioner	A	
Theatre Arts	A	
Welding Technology	A	C

A—Associate Degree Program C—Certificate Program

IMPERIAL VALLEY COLLEGE

380 E Aten Rd
Imperial CA 92251
760-355-6217
760-355-6172 Fax
www.imperial.edu

Efrain Silva, Dean of Economic and Workforce Development

Enrollment: Full-time 3,797 Part-time 4,067

Semester system

No Housing

OCCUPATIONAL PROGRAMS

Administration of Justice	A	C
Agricultural Business Management	A	C
Agricultural Crop Science		C
Air Conditioning and Refrigeration Technology	A	C
Alcohol and Drug Studies	A	C
Alternative Energy-Solar Technology		C
Automotive Collision Repair	A	C
Automotive Technology	A	C
Building Construction Technology	A	C
Carpentry Specialization		C
Concrete Masonry Specialization		C
Business		
Accounting Technician	A	C
Administration	A	
Administrative Assistant	A	C
Financial Services	A	C
Management	A	C
Marketing	A	C
Office Technician	A	C
Child Development	A	
Administration Specialization		C
Associate Teacher Specialization		C
Infant/Toddler Specialization		C
School-Age Specialization		C
CISCO CCNA Discovery	A	C
Computer Information Systems	A	
Correctional Science	A	C
Court Services Specialist		C
Early Childhood Education	A	
Electrical Technology	A	C
Electrical Wiring Specialization		C
Electronics Specialization		C
Solar Energy Specialization		C
Electrical Trades	A	C
Emergency Medical Services	A	
Energy Efficiency Technology	A	C
Firefighter I		C
Fire Technology	A	C
Journalism	A	
Legal Assistant	A	C
Medical Assistant		C
Multimedia and Web Development	A	C
Nursing		
LVN (Licensed Vocational Nurse)	A	C
RN (Registered Nurse)	A	
Pharmacy Technician	A	C
Water Treatment Systems Technology	A	C
Wastewater Treatment Specialization		C
Welding Technology	A	C

A—Associate Degree Program C—Certificate Program

IRVINE VALLEY COLLEGE

5500 Irvine Center Dr
Irvine CA 92618-0301
949-451-5100
949-451-5270 Fax
www.ivc.edu

Corine Doughty, Dean, Instruction, Education & Workforce Development

Enrollment: Full-time 7,797 Part-time 15,060

Semester system; Summer Session

No Housing

OCCUPATIONAL PROGRAMS

Program	A	C
Accounting		
Accounting	A	C
Computerized Accounting		C
Financial Accounting		C
Financial/Managerial Accounting		C
Income Tax		C
Payroll		C
Administration of Justice	A	
Law Enforcement	A	C
Supervision	A	C
Child Development		
Child Development	A	C
Infant/Toddler	A	C
School-Age Child	A	C
Computer Information Management		
Administrative Assistant	A	C
Computer Applications	A	C
Local Area Networks: (CISCO, A+, Network+, Linux+)	A	C
Web Authoring		C
Dance		
Commercial Dance		C
Dance Technique		C
Design Model Making and Rapid Prototyping	A	C
Digital Media Art/Interactive Media Art		
Animation for Games		C
Digital Media Art	A	C
Digital Photography		C
Drafting Technology		
Civil Computer-Aided Design		C
Computer-Aided Design	A	C
Mechanical Computer-Aided Design		C
Pre-Engineering		C
Electrical Technology		
Electrician Trainee		C
Energy Solar Photovoltaic Systems Technician		C
Electronic Technology		
Electronic Technology	A	C
Electronics Aide		C
Human Development		
Child Development (Human Development)	A	C
Early Childhood Assistant Teacher		C
Early Childhood Associate Teacher		C
Infant/Toddler (Human Development)	A	C
Kinesiology, Health and Athletics		
Coaching		C
Fitness Professional		C
Laser Technology: Photonics		C
Management		
Business Administration	A	
Business Management	A	C
Entrepreneurship Planning and Presentation		C
Entrepreneurship Skills		C
Idea Development and Opportunity Recognition for Entrepreneurs		C
Manufacturing Assistant	A	C
Research Tools for Entrepreneurs		C
Retail Management (WAFC)		C
Supervision	A	C
Understanding Entrepreneurial Operations		C
Paralegal Studies		
Paralegal Studies	A	C
Real Estate		
Real Estate	A	C
Sales		C
Sustainability and Resource Management		
Recycling and Resource Management		C
Recycling and Zero Waste		C
Theatre Arts		
Assistant Stage Manager		C
Live Entertainment Technician		C

A—Associate Degree Program C—Certificate Program

LAKE TAHOE COMMUNITY COLLEGE

One College Dr
South Lake Tahoe CA 96150-4524
530-541-4660
530-541-7852 Fax
www.ltcc.edu

Dr. Virginia Boyar, Dean of Career & Technical Education and Instruction

Enrollment: Full-time 644 Part-time 2,164

Quarter system; One 6-week summer session

No Housing

OCCUPATIONAL PROGRAMS

Accounting	A	C
Addiction Studies	A	C
Business	A	C
Commercial Music	A	C
Computer and Information Science	A	C
Computer Applications		C
Criminal Justice	A	C
Culinary Arts	A	C
Dental Assisting		C
Early Childhood Education	A	C
Emergency First Responder		C
Emergency Medical Technician		C
Environmental Technology and Sustainability	A	C
Fire Academy	A	C
Fire Officer	A	C
Fire Science	A	C
Medical Office Assistant	A	C
Nursing Assistant Training Program		C
Phlebotomy		C
Physical Therapy Aide		C
Wilderness Education/Search and Rescue	A	C

A—Associate Degree Program C—Certificate Program

LANEY COLLEGE

900 Fallon St
Oakland CA 94607-4893
510-834-5740
510-464-3231 Fax
www.laney.edu

Peter Crabtree, Dean of Career and Technical Education Division

Enrollment: Full-time 3,432 Part-time 24,089

Semester system; summer session: one 6-week, one 8-week

No Housing

OCCUPATIONAL PROGRAMS

Architectural		
Architectural Technology	A	C
Biological Sciences		
Biomanufacturing		C
Biomanufacturing Production	A	
Biomanufacturing Skills		C
Biomedical Engineering Technology		C
Business		
Accounting	A	C
Banking and Finance	A	C
Business Information System	A	C
Entrepreneurship		C
Management and Supervision	A	C
Marketing and Sales	A	C
Retail Management	A	C
Carpentry	A	C
Computer Information Science	A	
Construction Management	A	C
Build Codes and Inspections		C
Cosmetology	A	C
Culinary Arts		
Baking and Pastry	A	C
Cooking		C
Restaurant Management	A	C
Electricity/Electronics Technology		
Electrical Technology	A	C
Environmental Control Technology		
Building Automation Systems	A	C
Building Performance and Energy Efficiency		C
Commercial HVAC Systems	A	C
Refrigeration Technology		C
Residential and Light Commercial HVAC & R	A	C
Graphic Arts		
Applied Graphic Design/Digital Imaging	A	C
Labor Studies	A	C
Legal and Community Interpreting		C
Machine Technology	A	C
Industrial Maintenance Technology		C
Media Communications	A	C
Audio Production for Video, Broadcast and Digital Cinematography		C
Broadcast and Digital Cinematography AV Installation Technician		C
Performance and Production Video, Broadcast and Digital Cinematography	A	C
Video Production for Video, Broadcast and Digital Cinematography	A	C
Photography	A	C
Welding Technology	A	C
Wood Technology	A	C

A—Associate Degree Program C—Certificate Program

LAS POSITAS COLLEGE

3000 Campus Hill Drive
Livermore CA 94551-7650
925-424-1000
925-456-0705 Fax
www.laspositascollege.edu

Janice Noble, Ph.D., Vice President of Academic Services

Enrollment: Full-time 2,516 Part-time 4,908

Semester system; Summer Sessions: one 6-week, one 8-week

No Housing

OCCUPATIONAL PROGRAMS

Administration of Justice	A	
Automotive Electronics Technology	A	
Automotive Service Technician		C
Automotive Technician		C
Bookkeeping		C
Business		
Accounting Technician	A	
Administrative Assistant	A	C
Business	A	
Business Entrepreneurship	A	C
Business Retail Management		C
Business Workforce Proficiency		C
Marketing	A	C
Retailing Certificate		C
Retail Management		C
Supervisory Management		C
Computer Information Systems		
Computer Applications Software		C
Computer Information Systems	A	
Computer Networking Technology		
Cisco Network Associate		C
Cisco Network Professional		C
Computer Network Administration (Microsoft)		C
Computer Network Technician		C
Internetworking Technology & Cisco Administration	A	
Computer Science		
Computer Programming	A	C
Computer Programming for the Web	A	C
Design Technology	A	C
Early Childhood Development	A	
Associate Teacher Certificate		C
Basic Teacher Certificate		C
Family Childcare		C
Electronics Telecommunications Systems	A	C
Fire Service Technology	A	C
Horticulture	A	C
Industrial Technology	A	
Interior Design	A	C
Mass Communications: Journalism		C
Music		
Beginning Piano Pedagogy		C
Intermediate Piano Pedagogy		C
Occupational Safety and Health	A	C
Photography		C
Physical Education		
Coaching		C
Sport Medicine		C
Science Technology	A	
Visual Communication	A	C
Viticulture	A	C
Enology	A	C
Welding Technology	A	C

A—Associate Degree Program C—Certificate Program

LASSEN COLLEGE

Highway 139
P O Box 3000
Susanville CA 96130-3000
530-257-6181
530-251-8838 Fax
www.lassencollege.edu

Dr. Terri Armstrong, Vice President of Academic Services/AD

Enrollment: Full-time 881 Part-time 3,153

Semester system (Fall/Spring); Summer session

Co-ed Housing

OCCUPATIONAL PROGRAMS

Program	A	C
Accounting	A	
Administration of Justice	A	C
Reserve Officer Training		C
Agriculture Science and Technology	A	C
Agriculture Business		C
Animal Science		C
Horsemanship		C
Allied Health	A	
Art	A	
Studio Art	A	
Automotive Technology	A	
Advance Mechanics		C
Basic Mechanics		C
Electrical		C
Engine Repair		C
General Mechanics		C
Biological Science	A	
Business		
Entrepreneurship		C
Office Administrative Assistant	A	C
Child Development	A	C
Associate Teacher		C
Digital Graphic Design	A	C
Design Entrepreneurship		C
Fast Track I		C
Fast Track II		C
Fire Technology	A	C
Basic Fire Fighter		C
Geology	A	
Gunsmithing	A	C
Firearms Repair	A	C
Gunsmith Machinist and Metal Finishing		C
Long Guns		C
Pistolsmith		C
Riflesmith		C
Human Services	A	C
Drug and Alcohol Paraprofessional	A	C
Kinesiology	A	
Natural Science	A	
Nursing (Vocational)	A	C
Physical Education	A	
Welding Technology	A	C
Welding Technology 1–year Plan		C
Welding Technology 2–year Plan		C

A—Associate Degree Program C—Certificate Program

LONG BEACH CITY COLLEGE

4901 E Carson St
Long Beach CA 90808-1706
562-938-4111
www.lbcc.edu

Dr. Meena Singhal, Dean of Academic Services

Enrollment: Full-time 9,305 Part-time 13,316

Semester system; summer session

No Housing

OCCUPATIONAL PROGRAMS

Administration of Justice	A	C
Administrative Assistant	A	C
Advanced Transportation Technology		
Alternate Fuels	A	C
Electric Vehicles	A	C
Architectural Design	A	C
Baking and Pastry Arts	A	C
Business		
Accounting	A	C
General	A	C
International	A	C
Management	A	C
Marketing	A	C
Child Development	A	
Early Childhood Education	A	C
Special Education Assistant	A	C
Communication Studies	A	
Computer Networking	A	C
Computer Science	A	C
Culinary Arts	A	C
Customer Support	A	C
Dance	A	
Diagnostic Medical Imaging (Rad Tech)	A	C
Dietetics Program	A	C
Digital Design and Publication	A	C
Drafting		
Architectural	A	C
Mechanical Design (Occupational)	A	C
Electrical Technology	A	C
Engineering	A	
Family and Consumer Studies	A	C
Fashion Design	A	C
Assistant Designer	A	C
Pattern Maker		C
Sample Maker		C
Fashion Merchandising	A	C
Film	A	
Fire Science	A	C
Floral Design	A	C
Horticulture	A	C
Human Services	A	C
Alcohol and Drug Studies	A	C
Journalism	A	C
Kinesiology		
Recreation	A	
Teaching	A	
Library Technician	A	C
LVN to RN Career Ladder Program	A	C
Mechanical Maintenance Technology	A	C
Medical Assisting	A	C
Metal Fabrication Technology	A	C
Nursing		
RN	A	
LVN to RN Career Ladder Program	A	C
Photojournalism		C
Radio/Television		
Broadcast News	A	C
Performance	A	C
Multimedia Production		C
Theatre-General and Acting Academy	A	C
Tool Designer	A	C
Vocational/Practical	A	C

A—Associate Degree Program C—Certificate Program

LOS ANGELES CITY COLLEGE

855 N Vermont Ave
Los Angeles CA 90029-3590
323-953-4000
www.lacitycollege.edu

Semester system, 5 and 8 week summer session; 5 week winter session

Alex Davis, Dean of Economic Development and Workforce Education and Career Technical Education

Enrollment: Full-time 5,766 Part-time 12,254

No Housing

OCCUPATIONAL PROGRAMS

Administration of Justice	A	C
Administration of Justice – Specializing in Forensics		C
Evidence Specialist		C
Finger Print Classification		C
Investigations		C
Architecture		
Architectural and Interior Design		C
Computer Aided Design and Drawing		C
Technical Drawing		C
Art–Graphic Design	A	
Business Administration	A	C
Accounting	A	
Automated Accounting Technician		C
Bookkeeping	A	
Business Administration	A	C
Finance and Banking	A	C
Management	A	C
Marketing	A	C
Real Estate	A	C
Retail Management		C
Small Business Management		C
Child Development		
Child Development Associate Teacher		C
Child Development – Plan A	A	
Child Development – Plan B	A	
Child Development Site Supervisor		C
Child Development Teacher		C
Child Development Master Teacher		C
Children with Special Needs		C
Infant and Toddler Studies		C
Cinema/Television		
Beginning Film & TV Production		C
Cinema Production – Plan A	A	C
Cinema Production – Plan B	A	C
Cinema/Video Production		C
Cinematography		C
Directing		C
Television Production – Plan A	A	C
Television Production – Plan B	A	
Television Studio Production – Level I		C
Computer Applications & Office Technologies		
Administrative Medical Office Assistant	A	C
Administrative Office Assistant	A	C
Basic Administrative Assistant		C
Basic Administrative Medical Office Assistant		C
Basic Computer Applications		C
Basic Legal Office		C
Basic Medical Office Assistant		C
Basic Medical Transcription		C
Basic Web Page Design		C
Clerical Office Assistant		C
Computer Applications Specialist	A	C
Legal Office Assistant	A	C
Computer Sciences/Information Technology		
Applications Software		C
C++ Programming Language		C
Computer Information Systems	A	
Computer Networking Skills		C
Computer Technology	A	
Database Administration		C
Database Developer		C
JAVA Programming Language		C
Program in A+		C
Programming in Network+		C
Programming Languages		C
VBA Application		C
Web Client Technologies		C
Computer Technology	A	C
Program in A+ Certification		C
Program in Network+ Certification		C
Dental Technology	A	C
Advanced Prosthodontic, Implant and Maxillofacial		C
Esthetic		C
Master Dental		C
Dietetics		
Dietetic Service Supervisor		C
Dietetic Technician	A	
Electronics		
Basic Electronics		C
Electronic Systems Technology	A	C
Engineering – General	A	

A—Associate Degree Program C—Certificate Program

LOS ANGELES CITY COLLEGE (continued)

Journalism	A	
Kinesology		C
Law		
Paralegal Studies	A	
Music	A	
Music Copyist		C
Music Technology		C
Instrumental Performer/Brass		C
Instrumental Performer/Guitar		C
Instrumental Performer/Percussion		C
Instrumental Performer/Piano		C
Instrumental Performer/Strings		C
Instrumental Performer/Woodwinds		C
Orchestrator/Arranger		C
Vocal Performer		C
Nursing		
Certified Nursing Assistant		C
Home Health Aide		C
Nursing, Registered	A	
Photography		
Applied Photography	A	
Photography – Commercial		C
Photography – Dark Room		C
Photography – Digital		C
Photography – Freelance		C
Photography – Photojournalism		C
Psychology		
Human Services – Drug/Alcohol	A	C
Human Services – Generalist	A	C
Radiologic Technology	A	
Theater		
Theater Academy – Acting	A	C
Theater Academy – Advanced Acting		C
Theater Academy – Costume Design		C
Theater Academy – Technical Theater		C
Theater – General	A	
Professional Actor Training		C

A—Associate Degree Program C—Certificate Program

LOS ANGELES HARBOR COLLEGE

1111 Figueroa PL
Wilmington CA 90744-2397
310-233-4000
310-953-4013 Fax
www.lahc.edu

Semester system, 8 & 5-week summer session, 4-week winter session

Sandra Sanchez, Dean of Occupational Education/CTE
Dr. Stephanie Atkinson-Alston, Dean of Academic Affairs and Curriculum

Enrollment: Full-time 2,314 Part-time 7,403

No Housing

OCCUPATIONAL PROGRAMS

Administration of Justice	A	C
Architectural Technology	A	C
Business	A	
Accounting	A	
Business Administration	A	C
Child Development	A	C
Computer Applications and Office Technologies (CAOT)		
Accounting Clerk		C
Administrative Assistant	A	
Computer Information Systems	A	
Legal Office Assistant	A	C
Medical Office Assistant	A	C
Microcomputer Applications		C
Office Administration		C
Office Automation		C
Computer Technology	A	C
Culinary Arts	A	C
Fire Technology	A	C
Nursing		
LVN to RN	A	
Nursing Professional RN	A	
Real Estate	A	C

A—Associate Degree Program C—Certificate Program

LOS ANGELES MISSION COLLEGE

LOS ANGELES MISSION COLLEGE

13356 Eldridge Ave
Sylmar CA 91342-32941
818-364-7600
818-364-7755 Fax
www.lamission.edu

Semester system

Leonard S. Baptiste, Dean of Academic Affairs

Enrollment: Full-time and Part-time 10,275

No Housing

OCCUPATIONAL PROGRAMS

Accounting	A	
Administration of Justice	A	
Basic Police Academy Preparation		C
Probation/Correction Officer Candidate		C
Business Administration	A	
Child Development	A	C
Bilingual/Bicultural Preschool	A	C
Child Development in Administration		C
Early Childhood Education	A	
Family Child Care	A	C
Infant/Toddler	A	C
Preschool	A	C
School-Age Care	A	C
Special Needs	A	C
Computer Applications and Office Technology	A	
Communications		C
Computer Applications		C
Office Assistant		C
Computer Science–Information Technology	A	
Business Emphasis	A	
Microcomputer Applications		C
Microcomputer Applications Management		C
Family and Consumer Studies		
Consumer Education and Management	A	C
Dietary Services Supervisor		C
Foods and Nutrition	A	
Gerontology	A	C
Introduction to Hospitality		C
Marriage and Family Life	A	
Nutrition		C
Restaurant Management		C
Finance	A	
Food Service Management		
Baking		C
Culinary Arts		C
Food Management Production Services and Related Techniques	A	
Food Service Management		C
Restaurant Management		C
Health Sciences	A	
Interior Design	A	C
Introduction to Interior Design		C
Introduction to Space Planning		C
Technology and Interior Design		C
Legal Assisting (Paralegal)	A	C
Management	A	
Retail Management		C
Marketing	A	
Multimedia Studies		
Advanced Skills in Animation and 3D Design		C
Advanced Skills in Graphic and Web Design		C
Advanced Skills in Video Production		C
Animation and 3D Design	A	C
Graphic and Web Design	A	C
Video Production	A	C

A—Associate Degree Program C—Certificate Program

LOS ANGELES PIERCE COLLEGE

6201 Winnetka Ave
Woodland Hills CA 91371-0001
818-347-0551
818-710-4436 Fax
www.piercecollege.edu

Jose Luis Fernandez, Dean, Academic Affairs and Career and Technical Education

Enrollment: Full-time 5,594 Part-time 14,194

Semester system; 2 summer sessions and 1 winter session (5 weeks each)

No Housing

OCCUPATIONAL PROGRAMS

Program		
Addiction Studies	A	C
Agriculture		
General Agriculture	A	C
Horse Science	A	C
Horticulture		
Floral Design and Management		C
Gardening (Advanced)		C
General Horticulture	A	
Landscape Planning and Design	A	
Pre-Veterinary Medicine	A	
Veterinary Technology	A	
American Sign Language (Interpreting)	A	
Architecture		
Architectural Technology	A	C
Art	A	
Ceramic Design	A	
Graphic Design	A	C
Graphic Design for the Web		C
Business Administration		
Accounting	A	
General Business	A	
International Business		C
Management and Supervision	A	
Marketing	A	C
Retail Management (WAFC)		C
Tax Preparation		C
Child Development	A	
Associate Teacher		C
Infant Care Teacher		C
Preschool		C
Preschool Director		C
Preschool Teacher		C
School Age Child Care Teacher		C
Computer Applications & Office Technologies		
Administrative Professional	A	C
Basic Computerized Accounting		C
Basic Internet		C
Basic Word Processing: Microsoft Word for Windows		C
Computer Applications		C
Desktop Publishing		C
General Administrative	A	C
Legal Office Procedures	A	C
Legal Office Skills		C
Office Administration: Advanced Computer Applications		C
Office Clerical		C
Office Communications		C
Web Site Construction and Maintenance		C
Computer Science		
Computer and Networking Technology	A	
Personal Computer Service Technology		C
Programming for Business	A	C
Programming for Computer Science	A	
Networking Technology		C
Web Development		C
Web Development, Programming and Scripting		C
Criminal Justice	A	
Electronics and Electric Technology		
Analog Option		C
Communications Option		C
Digital Option		C
Electronics	A	
Engineering Graphics and Design Technology	A	C
Environmental Science and Technology	A	
Industrial Technology		
Automotive Emission Specialist		C
Automotive Light Service Tech		C
Automotive Performance Applications		C
Automotive Powertrain Specialist		C
Automotive Service Technology	A	C
Numerical Control Programming	A	C
Music	A	
Nursing	A	
Photojournalism	A	
Theater Arts	A	
Costume Option	A	
Technical Theater Option	A	C

A—Associate Degree Program C—Certificate Program

LOS ANGELES SOUTHWEST COLLEGE

1600 W Imperial Hwy
Los Angeles CA 90047-4899
323-241-5225
323-241-5476 Fax
www.lasc.edu

Rick Hodge, Dean, Career Technical Education

Enrollment: Full-time 1,530 Part-time 4,689

Semester system; Two 5 week summer sessions

No Housing

OCCUPATIONAL PROGRAMS

Program	A	C
Administration of Justice	A	C
Fingerprinting		C
Business Administration		
Accounting/General Business	A	
Banking & Finance	A	C
Bookkeeping		C
Business and Technology Skills		C
Economics	A	
Finance		C
Income Tax Form		C
Management		C
Management/Supervision	A	C
Small Business Entrepreneurship I		C
Small Business Entrepreneurship II		C
Supervision		C
Child Development	A	
Director, Private Licensed Preschool		C
Teacher, Private Licensed Preschool		C
Bilingual-Bicultural Children		C
Differently Abled Children		C
Infant Toddler		C
School Age Children		C
Computer Applications—Office Technology	A	
Advanced Office Technology		C
Basic Office Technology		C
General Office Assistant		C
Legal Office Assistant		C
Microsoft Excel		C
Microsoft Word		C
Receptionist		C
Word Processor		C
Computer Science-Information Technology	A	
Drafting	A	C
Education: Teacher Assistant		C
Electronics Technology	A	C
Automated Manufacturing		C
Computer Servicing		C
Quality Control		C
Telecom and Network		C
Journalism	A	
Law/Paralegal	A	
Law Office Specialist I		C
Law Office Specialist-Civil Law		C
Law Office Specialist-Litigation		C
Nursing-Registered	A	
Physical Education-Flexercise		C
Psychology		
Chemical Dependency Counselor		C
Real Estate		C
Appraisal		C
Broker		C
Escrow		C
Salesperson		C
Speech Communication		C
Early Childhood Speech Therapy Assistant		C
Theater Arts	A	

A—Associate Degree Program C—Certificate Program

LOS ANGELES TRADE-TECHNICAL COLLEGE

400 W Washington Blvd
Los Angeles CA 90015-4181
213-763-7000
www.lattc.edu

Virginia Berry, Dean of CTE and Instruction

Enrollment: Approximate 14,000

Semester system; Two 6 week summer sessions/Winter intersession

No Housing

OCCUPATIONAL PROGRAMS

Program	A	C
Administration of Justice		
Correctional Science	A	C
Architectural Technology	A	C
Art Trades		
Sign Graphics	A	C
Visual Communications		C
Automotive Collision Repair	A	C
Automotive Technology		
Automotive and Related Technology	A	C
Diesel and Related Technology	A	C
Hybrid and Electrical Plug-In Vehicle Technology		C
Motorcycle Repair Mechanics		C
Tune-Up		C
Business		
Accounting	A	
Accounting Clerk		C
Carpentry	A	C
Construction Technologies	A	C
Chemical Technology	A	C
Child Development/Early Care and Education		
Child Development Plan A	A	
Child Development Plan B	A	
Early Childhood Education	A	
Infant/Toddler Teacher		C
Preschool Associate Teacher		C
Preschool Teacher		C
School Age Program Teacher		C
Site Supervisor		C
Teacher with Special Needs		C
Community Planning & Economic Development		C
Computer Applications and Office Technology		
Administrative Assistant	A	C
Information Processing Specialist	A	C
Medical Office Assistant		C
Office Assistant–Clerical	A	C
Computer Information Systems	A	C
Construction Technology	A	
Carpentry	A	C
Plumbing	A	C
Plumbing Construction Technology	A	C
Cosmetology, Skin Therapy and Barbering	A	C
Skin Therapy		C
Culinary Arts	A	C
Baking, Professional	A	C
Restaurant Management	A	
Electrical		
Electrical Construction and Maintenance	A	C
Electrical Construction and Maintenance: Construction Technologies	A	C
Electronics		
Electronic Communications	A	C
Microcomputer Technician	A	C
Environmental Control Technology		
Energy Systems Technology Fundamentals		C
Operation and Maintenance Engineering: Steam Plant		C
Refrigeration and Air Conditioning Mechanics		C
Renewable Energy: Energy Efficiency Emphasis	A	
Renewable Energy Technician: Solar PV Installation and Maintenance	A	
Renewable Energy Technician: Solar Thermal	A	
Solar PV Installation and Maintenance Technician		C
Solar Thermal Installation and Maintenance Technician		C
Weatherization and Energy Efficiency		C
Fashion Careers		
Fashion Design	A	C
Fashion Merchandising	A	C
Fashion Technology	A	C
Tailoring		C
Industrial Systems Technology and Maintenance		
Powerline Mechanic		C
Renewable Energy Generation, Transmission and Distribution w. Powerline Mechanic Emphasis	A	
Utility Industry Fundamentals		C
Labor Studies	A	C
Machine Shop CNC	A	C
Management/Supervision	A	C

A—Associate Degree Program C—Certificate Program

LOS ANGELES TRADE-TECHNICAL COLLEGE continued

Marketing and Public Relations	A	C
Microcomputer Technician	A	C
Nursing		
Registered Nursing	A	
Operating and Maintenance Engineer Steam Plant		C
Process Plant Technology	A	C
Real Estate	A	C
Retail Merchandising	A	
Sign Graphics	A	C
Visual Communications	A	C
Small Business Entrepreneurship		C
Solid Waste Management Technology		C
Street Maintenance Technology	A	C
Water and Wastewater Technology		
Supply Water Systems Technology		C
Wastewater Systems Technology	A	
Water Systems Technology: Supply Water Technology	A	
Welding Technology		
Welding, Gas and Electric	A	C
Welding, Gas and Electric: Construction Technologies		C

A—Associate Degree Program C—Certificate Program

LOS ANGELES VALLEY COLLEGE

5800 Fulton Ave
Van Nuys CA 91401-4096
818-947-2600
818-947-2620 Fax
www.lavc.edu

Karen Daar, Vice President Academic Affairs

Enrollment: Full-time 18,000 Part-time 4,592

Two 15-week semesters; one 5-week winter intersession; Two 5-week summer semesters

No Housing

OCCUPATIONAL PROGRAMS

Accounting	A	C
Administration of Justice	A	C
Architecture		C
Art–Graphic Design	A	C
Banking and Finance	A	C
Bank Management		C
Bilingual Teacher Aide		C
Biomedical Equipment Technology		C
Broadcasting	A	
Performance	A	C
Radio	A	C
Television	A	C
Business	A	
Business Management		C
C/C++		C
Child Development	A	
Associate Teacher, Preschool		C
Associate Teacher, Preschool Literacy		C
Director, Preschool		C
Early Childhood Education	A	
Infant/Toddler Care Teacher		C
School Age Day Care		C
Special Education	A	C
Teacher		C
Cinema Arts	A	
Cinema Styles		C
Commercial Music	A	
Instrumental/Vocal Performer		C
Jazz Studies		C
Music Arranging		C
Music Notation		C
Music Technology		C
Computer Applications and Office Technology		
Administrative Assistant	A	C
Computer Applications Specialist	A	C
General Office Assistant		C
Website Software Specialist		C
Computer Graphics/Design		C
Computer Science	A	
Computer Science Programming		C
Correctional Science	A	C
Electronics	A	
Biomedical Instrumentation	A	C
Technician		C
Technology		C
Engineering	A	
Industrial/Manufacturing	A	C
Mechanical Engineering	A	
Fire Technology	A	C
Homeland Security		C
Journalism	A	
Magazine	A	C
Newspaper	A	C
Photojournalism	A	C
Management	A	C
Manufacturing Technology		
Metal Machining	A	C
Numerical Control	A	C
Marketing		C
Mechanical Drafting Design		C
Mechanical Engineering Technology		C
Media Arts		
Directing	A	C
Post-Production	A	C
Producing	A	C
Screenwriting	A	C
Microcomputers Application Mgt Specialist		C
Microcomputer Systems		C
Motion Picture Production Technician		C
Property Management		C
Real Estate	A	C
Registered Nurse	A	
Respiratory Therapist	A	C
Solar Energy Design and Management	A	C
Sustainable Construction Management	A	C
Technology–A+Certification Preparation		C
Theater Arts	A	
Acting	A	
Directing		C
Music Theater		C
Production		C
Technical	A	
Theatrical Performance		C

A—Associate Degree Program C—Certificate Program

LOS MEDANOS COLLEGE

2700 E Leland Rd
Pittsburg CA 94565-5197
925-439-2181
925-439-7841 Fax
www.losmedanos.edu

Natalie Hannum, Dean of Career Technical Education

Enrollment: Full-time 3,219 Part-time 6,747

Semester system

No Housing

OCCUPATIONAL PROGRAMS

Program		
Acting	A	
Administration of Justice	A	
Basic Law Enforcement Academy		C
Basic Law Enforcement Academy Advanced		C
Basic Law Enforcement Academy Intensive		C
Basic Law Enforcement Academy Module III		C
Criminal Investigations		C
Criminal Law		C
Appliance Service Technology	A	C
Electrical Appliance Technician		C
Heating, Ventilation and Air Conditioning Specialist		C
Refrigeration Technician		C
Art		
Graphics Communication	A	C
Automotive Technology	A	C
Air Conditioning Specialist		C
Automotive Chassis Specialist		C
Engine Performance		C
Engine Repair and Machine Specialist		C
Smog Technician Specialist		C
Transmission Specialist		C
Business		
Accounting	A	C
Office Administration	A	C
Retail Management		C
Small Business Management and Operations	A	C
Child Development	A	C
Assistant Teacher		C
Associate Teacher		C
Infant Toddler Care		C
School-Age Associate Teacher		C
School-Age Child Care		C
School-Age Development and Education		C
Site Supervisor/Program Director		C
Special Needs Care and Education		C
Computer Science	A	
Computer Support Specialist	A	
Computer Support Specialist-Advanced		C
Computer Support Specialist-Basic		C
Core Competencies		C
Foundation		C
Game Design		C
Microcomputer Systems Specialist		C
Network and Security	A	
Networking and Security-Advanced		C
Networking and Security-Basic		C
PC Repair Technician (A+ Certification)		C
Web Design		C
Electrical Technology	A	C
Instrumentation Technology	A	C
Emergency Medical Services		C
EMS Recertification		C
Engineering	A	
Fire Technology	A	C
Fire Academy		C
Fire Prevention		C
Fire Protection		C
Journalism	A	
Management and Supervision	A	C
Music	A	
Commercial Music		
Business Management		C
Pedagogy		C
Performance		C
Recording Arts	A	C
Nursing		
Registered	A	
Vocational		C
Process Technology	A	C
Real Estate	A	C
Travel Marketing	A	C
Cruise Specialist		C
Home-Based Travel Specialist		C
Welding Technology	A	C

A—Associate Degree Program C—Certificate Program

MARIN COMMUNITY COLLEGE

COLLEGE OF MARIN

Kentfield Campus
835 Colllege Ave
Kentfield CA 94904-2590

Indian Valley Campus
1800 Ignacio Blvd
Novato CA 94949
415-457-8811
415-884-0417 Fax
www.marin.edu

Semester system; 6 week summer session

Dean of Workforce Development, College and Community Partnerships

Enrollment: Full-time and Part-time 8,590

No Housing

OCCUPATIONAL PROGRAMS

Administration of Justice	A	C
Automotive Collision Repair Technology	A	C
Automotive Technology	A	C
Business		
Administration	A	
Applied Accounting	A	C
General	A	C
Management	A	C
Business Office Systems		
Office Management	A	C
Computer Information System	A	C
Court Reporting	A	C
Dental Assisting: Registered	A	C
Early Childhood Education	A	C
Environmental Landscaping	A	C
Machine and Metals Technology	A	C
Medical Assistant	A	C
Administrative	A	C
Clinical	A	C
Nursing: Registered (RN)	A	
Real Estate	A	C

A—Associate Degree Program C—Certificate Program

MENDOCINO COLLEGE

1000 Hensley Creek Rd
Ukiah CA 95482
707-468-3002
707-463-6529 Fax
www.mendocino.edu

Semester System

Steve Hixenbaugh, Interim, Dean of Career and Technical Education and Lake Center Instruction

Enrollment: Full-time 1,232 Part-time 3,338

No Housing

OCCUPATIONAL PROGRAMS

Administration of Justice	A	C
Agriculture		
Horticulture	A	
Landscape Practices		C
Nursery Production		C
Sustainable Small Farms Management		C
Viticulture Skills		C
Alcohol and Other Drugs Studies	A	C
Automotive Technology		
Chassis Specialist		C
Technician		C
Technology	A	
Tune-Up and Electronic Specialist		C
Business		
Accounting	A	C
Administration	A	
Entrepreneurship		C
Management	A	C
Real Estate	A	C
Retail Management		C
Business Office Technology		
Administrative Assistant	A	
Legal		C
Medical		C
Medical Billing/Coding		C
Ceramics-Master Technician		C
Child Development/Family Relations	A	C
Computer and Information Sciences	A	
Computer Applications & Office Administration	A	C
Culinary Arts Management		C
Firefighter I		C
Fire Officer		C
Fire Science	A	
Human Services Paraprofessional		C
Human Service Worker		C
Nursing		
LVN to RN Career Ladder	A	C
Registered Nurse	A	
Physical Education/Kinesiology	A	
Recording Arts and Technology		C
Sustainable Technology		
Construction		C
Renewable Energy		C
Residential Performance and Efficiency		C
Textiles		
Clothing Construction		C
Weaving		C
Theatre Arts		
Dance	A	
Theatre	A	

A—Associate Degree Program C—Certificate Program

MERCED COLLEGE

3600 M St
Merced CA 95348-2898
209-384-6000
209-384-6338 Fax
www.mccd.edu

Semester system; 6 week summer sessions

Mary K. Gilliland, Vice President, Instruction

Enrollment: Full-time 4,253 Part-time 5,313

No Housing

OCCUPATIONAL PROGRAMS

Accounting	A	C
Addiction Studies	A	C
Administrative Office Management		
Medical Office Professional	A	C
Office Professional	A	C
Agriculture		
Agricultural Chemicals		C
General Agriculture	A	C
General Agriculture: Advanced	A	
Agriculture Business	A	C
Advanced	A	
Animal Science	A	C
Advanced	A	
Automotive Technology	A	
Body and Fender		C
Engine Performance		C
Master Auto Technology	A	C
Suspension and Brakes		C
Transmissions		C
Biotechnology	A	C
Business Administration	A	
Business, General	A	C
Child Development		
Child Development	A	
Early Childhood Education	A	
Early Intervention Assistant Specialization		C
Families in Crisis Specialization		C
Infant/Toddler Care Specialization		C
School Age Care Specialization		C
Communication Studies	A	
Computer Sciences		
Computer Science	A	
Management Information System	A	
Corrections	A	C
Criminal Justice	A	C
Administration of Justice	A	
Crop Science	A	C
Customer Service Academy Certificate		C
Diesel Equipment Technology	A	C
Dietetic Services Supervisor		C
Drafting Technology		
CAD Drafting–Architectural Design	A	C
CAD Drafting–Mechanical Design	A	C
CAD Draftsman–Architectural		C
CAD Operator		C
Electronics/Electrical and Computer Technologies		
Computer and Networking Technology	A	C
Electrical Technology	A	C
Electronics Technician	A	C
Instrumentation and Process Control Technology	A	C
Mechatronics/Automated Systems Technology	A	C
Emergency Medical Technician		C
Engineering Technology	A	
Entrepreneurship		
Small Business Entrepreneurship	A	C
Environmental Technologies	A	C
Fire Technology	A	C
Foods and Nutrition	A	C
Foster Care Education Certificate of Specialization		C
Health Sciences	A	
Heating, Ventilation, Air Conditioning, and Refrigeration Technology		
HVAC–Commercial Refrigeration Technician		C
HVAC Technician	A	C
Horse Management	A	C
Horseshoeing–Advanced		C
Horseshoeing-Beginning		C
Human Services	A	C
Industrial Maintenance Technology		C
Journalism	A	
Laboratory Technology	A	
Landscape Horticulture	A	C
Management/Supervisory Training	A	C
Mechanized Agriculture Technology	A	C
Compact Power Equipment		C
Merchandising Management	A	C
Music		
Guitar	A	
Instrumental	A	
Piano	A	
Vocal	A	

A—Associate Degree Program C—Certificate Program

MERCED COLLEGE continued

Program	A	C
Nursing		
Assistant		C
Registered	A	
Vocational	A	C
Photography	A	C
Physical Education	A	
Radiologic Technology	A	C
Real Estate	A	C
Sonography		
Diagnostic Medical Sonography		C
Diagnostic Medical Sonography: Cardiac Track		C
Virtual Office Professional		C
Welding Technology	A	C
Advanced Welding and Metal Fabrication		C

MERRITT COLLEGE

12500 Campus Dr
Oakland CA 94619
510-531-4911
510-436-2654 Fax
www.merritt.edu

Semester system, 6 week summer session

Dr. Elmer Bugg, Vice President of Instruction

Enrollment: Full-time 1,999 Part-time 4,477

No Housing

OCCUPATIONAL PROGRAMS

Administration of Justice	A	C
Corrections	A	C
Police Science	A	C
Art		
Botanical Illustration		C
Business		
Accounting	A	C
Administrative Assistant	A	C
Administrative Office Systems & Applications	A	
Business Administration	A	
Business Information Processing	A	C
Business Management		C
Entrepreneurship		C
General Business	A	
Human Resource Management		C
Legal Office Assistant		C
Retail Management		C
Small Business Management		C
Child Development	A	
Assistant Teacher		C
Associate Teacher		C
Teacher		C
Chronic Care Assistant		C
Communication	A	
Community Social Service	A	C
Substance Abuse	A	C
Computer Information Systems		
PC Applications Help Desk Specialist		C
Web Page Authoring		C
Web Publishing		C
Educational Technology		
Online Teaching		C
Emergency Medical Technician I		C
Environmental Management and Technology		
Environmental Management Fundamentals		C
Greening the Urban Environment		C
Urban Agroecology		C
Health Services	A	
Human Services		C
Kinesiology		
Personal Trainer		C
Landscape Horticulture		
Basic Landscape Horticulture		C
Intermediate Landscape & Parks Maintenance		C
Intermediate Landscape Design & Construction		C
Intermediate Nursery Management		C
Landscape and Parks Maintenance Specialist	A	C
Landscape Architecture	A	
Landscape Design & Construction Specialist	A	C
Permaculture Design		C
Medical Assisting		
Clinical Medical Assisting		C
Nursing (Associate Degree)	A	
Nutrition and Dietetics		
Dietary Manager (Dietetic Service Supervisor)		C
Dietary Technology	A	
Pathway II Certificate		C
Radiologic Technology	A	C
Paralegal Studies	A	C
Real Estate	A	C
Vocational Nursing	A	C

A—Associate Degree Program C—Certificate Program

MIRACOSTA COLLEGE

One Barnard Dr
Oceanside CA 92056-3899
760-757-2121
760-795-6804 Fax
www.miracosta.edu

Al Taccone, Ph.D., Dean, Career and Technical Education

Enrollment: Full-time 6,143 Part-time 13,363

Semester system; Summer session

No Housing

OCCUPATIONAL PROGRAMS

Accounting	A	C
Billing, Cost and Accounting Assistant		C
Bookkeeping	A	C
Income Tax Preparer		C
Administration of Justice		
Criminology and Justice Studies	A	
Law Enforcement	A	C
Art		
Digital Photography	A	C
Automotive Technology	A	C
Automotive Alignment Brakes and Suspension		C
Automotive Electronics		C
Automotive Electronics, Computers,and Emissions and/or HVAC		C
Automotive Quick Service Assistant		C
Automotive Repair: Drive-Train Specialist		C
Basic Engine Performance		C
California Smog Check Technician		C
Biotechnology		
Bioprocess Technology		C
Laboratory Skills		C
Research and Development	A	C
Business Administration	A	
Business Fundamentals		C
Entrepreneurship	A	C
Entrepreneurship Fundamentals		C
Management	A	C
Marketing	A	C
Project Management		C
Retail Assistant		C
Retail Management	A	C
Social Media for Business		C
Business Office Technology		
Administrative Professional	A	C
Office Assistant		C
Office Manager	A	C
Child Development		
Assistant Teacher		C
Associate Teacher	A	C
Early Intervention and Inclusion		C
Master Teacher	A	C
Site Supervisor	A	C
Teacher	A	C
Computer Science	A	
Computer Programing Fundamentals	A	C
Computer Studies and Information Technology		
Certified Computer Desktop Support Specialist		C
Computer Applications Professional for Business	A	C
Computer Applications User		C
Computer Competencies for the Workplace		C
Computer Studies	A	C
E-commerce		C
Emerging Technologies in Computer Studies		C
Microsoft Certified Application Specialist for Business		C
Network and Desktop Systems Administration	A	C
Dance	A	
Dance Instructor		C
Pilates Instructor		C
Design		
3D Modeling and Prototyping		C
Applied Design		C
Architectural Design	A	C
Computer-Aided Drafting	A	C
Computer-Aided Drafting & Design	A	C
Construction Management		C
Drafting Fundamental		C
Engineering Design Graphics		C
Mechanical Design	A	C
Dramatic Arts	A	
Design and Technology	A	C
Gerontology	A	
Optimal Aging and Older Adulthood		C
Horticulture		
Irrigation Technology		C
Landscape Architecture	A	C
Landscape Management	A	C
Nursery/Horticulture Crop Production	A	C
Wine and Viticulture Technology		C

A—Associate Degree Program C—Certificate Programs

MIRACOSTA COLLEGE (continued)

Hospitality		
Catering Operations		C
Dining Room Operations		C
Food Service Operations		C
Front Office Operations		C
Hospitality Management	A	C
Meeting and Event Management		C
Restaurant Management	A	C
Rooms Division Management		C
Kinesiology	A	
Personal Fitness Trainer		C
Yoga Instructor		C
Massage		
Holistic Health Practitioner (1,000 Hours)		C
Massage Therapist (500 Hours)		C
Media Arts and Technologies		
Graphic Communication		C
Graphic Design	A	C
Digital and Print Publishing		C
Video and Animation		C
Video and Media Design		C
Web Design		C
Web Development and Design	A	C
Medical Administrative Professional		
Medical Insurance and Coding Specialist		C
Medical Office Professional	A	C
Medical Office Specialist		C
Music		
Audio Recording Production	A	C
Business of Music		C
Digital Audio		C
Live Performance Audio		C
Music Performance	A	
Performance Technician		C
Nursing		
Certified Nursing Assistant		C
Home Health Aide		C
Licensed Vocational Nursing	A	C
Registered Nursing (ADN)	A	
Registered Nursing (LVN to RN)	A	
Nutrition		
Fitness Nutrition Specialist		C
Psychology	A	
Human Development	A	
Research Fundamentals		C
Volunteer Services		C
Real Estate	A	C
Assistant		C
Entrepreneurship	A	C
Finance		C
Property Management		C
Sales		C
Sociology		
Research Fundamentals		C
Volunteer Services		C
Spanish	A	
Career Spanish for Medical Personnel		C
Surgical Technology	A	C

A—Associate Degree Program C—Certificate Program

MISSION COLLEGE

3000 Mission College Blvd
Santa Clara CA 95054-1897
408-988-2200
www.missioncollege.org

Mina Jahan, Dean, Applied Science

Enrollment: Full-time 3,000 Part-time 7,000

Semester system; 6 week summer session

No Housing

OCCUPATIONAL PROGRAMS

Program	A	C
Accounting	A	C
Business	A	
Business Communications		C
Business Computing		C
Business Essentials		C
Business Professional		C
E–Business		C
Global Business		C
Small Business Start-up		C
Child Development	A	C
Early Childhood Education	A	
Early Intervention Assistant		C
Family Child Care		C
Master Teacher		C
Communication Studies	A	C
Computer Applications		
Computer Application Level II		C
Help Desk Specialist		C
Microsoft Office		C
Office Administration	A	C
Office Information Systems	A	C
Office Support Specialist		C
Professional Internet Skills		C
Computer Science & Information Technology (CSIT)	A	C
C/C++/Unix Programming		C
Certified Network Engineer (CNE)		C
Cisco Certified Network Administration (CCNA)	C	
Cisco Certified Network Professional (CCNP)		C
Computer Information Systems		C
Computer Network Technology	A	C
Computer Programming		C
Linux System Administration		C
Microsoft Certified Database Administration (MCDBA)		C
Microsoft Windows Server		C
Net Programming		C
Oracle Database Administration (DBA)		C
Creative Arts Entrepreneurship		C
Digital Illustration		C
Digital Music		C
Engineering	A	
Fire Technology	A	
Emergency Medical Technician I Certification		C
Firefighter I Certification		C
Global Studies		C
Graphic Arts-Design	A	C
Graphic Design	A	C
Marketing Communication		C
Multimedia		C
Video Game Art and Design		C
Web Design		C
Web Developer		C
Health Occupations		
Acute Care Nurse Assistant		C
Childbirth Trainer		C
Community Health Worker	A	C
Community Health Worker for the Developmentally Disabled	A	C
Home Health Aide		C
LVN to RN	A	
Nursing Assistant Level 1		C
Psychiatric Technician	A	C
Vocational Nursing	A	C
Hospitality Management	A	
Culinary Arts		C
Food Services and Restaurant Management		C
Fundamental Food Services Skills I		C
Kinesiology		
Fitness Specialist (Personal Trainer Emphasis)	A	C
Real Estate	A	
Broker		C
Sales		C
Retail Floristry		C

A—Associate Degree Program C—Certificate Program

MODESTO JUNIOR COLLEGE

435 College Ave
Modesto CA 95350-9977
209-575-6058
209-575-6025 Fax
www.mjc.edu

Susan Kincade, Vice President of Instruction

Enrollment: Full-time 4,304 Part-time 10,557

Semester System; 6 Week Summer Session

No Housing

OCCUPATIONAL PROGRAMS

Administration of Justice	A	
Agriculture & Environmental Sciences		
Agriculture Business	A	
Agriculture–Sales, Service Technician	A	C
Animal Science	A	
Artificial Insemination Technician		C
Commercial Floristry Technician		C
Crop Science	A	
Dairy Science	A	
Environmental Horticultural Science	A	
Forestry	A	C
Fruit Science	A	
Landscape Design		C
Landscape/Parks Maintenance		C
Mechanized Agriculture	A	
Mechanized Agriculture Technician		C
Nursery Production		C
Poultry Science	A	
Recreational Land Management	A	C
Soil Science	A	
Veterinary Technician		C
Allied Health		
Medical Assisting	A	C
Nursing Assistant (CNA)		C
Nursing, LVN 30-Unit Option		C
Nursing, LVN to ADN Advanced Placement Pathway	A	
Nursing, RN	A	
Respiratory Care	A	C
Arts, Humanities, & Communications		
Photography	A	
Recording Arts		C
Theatre Performance		C
Behavioral & Social Sciences		
Human Services		C
Supervisory Management in Public Safety	A	C
Business Administration	A	
Accounting	A	C
Accounting Clerk		C
Bookkeeping	A	C
Business Operations: Management	A	
Clerical	A	C
International Business		C
Marketing	A	
Office Administration	A	C
Office Support		C
Professional Selling		C
Word Processing		C
Computer Science	A	
Computer Electronics	A	C
Computer Graphics Applications	A	
Computer Information Systems	A	
Computer Programming Specialist		C
Office Computer Applications		C
Records Management/Data Entry Specialist		C
Family & Consumer Sciences		
Associate Teacher		C
Child Development	A	
Early Interventionist		C
Master Teacher		C
Site Supervisor		C
Supervisory Management		C
Teacher		C
Kinesiology		
Athletic Training/Sports Medicine	A	
Public Safety		
Emergency Medical Technician		C
Fire Academy		C
Fire Science	A	C
Technical Education		
Advanced Heavy Equipment Technician		C
Autobody/Collision Repair	A	C
Autobody Refinishing	A	C
Automotive Engines and Transmissions		C
Automotive Maintenance		C
Automotive Technician	A	C
Basic Heavy Equipment Technician		C
CNC Operator		C
CNC Programmer		C
CSU-GE Pattern		C
Design and Fabrication		C
Design and Technical Theatre		C
Gas Metal Arc Welding		C
Gas Tungsten Arc Welding		C
Heavy Machinery Management		C
IGETC Pattern	A	

A—Associate Degree Program C—Certificate Program

MODESTO JUNIOR COLLEGE (continued)

Technical Education continued		
Industrial Electronics	A	C
Machine Tool Technology	A	C
Maintenance Electrician	A	C
Maintenance Machinist 1		C
Maintenance Machinist 2		C
Maintenance Mechanic		C
Pipe Welding		C
Real Estate	A	C
Real Estate Sales Person		C
Sheet Metal Fabricator		C
Shielded Metal Arc Welding		C
Technician		C
Welding	A	C

MONTEREY PENINSULA COLLEGE

980 Fremont Blvd
Monterey CA 93940-4799
831-646-4000
831-655-2627 Fax
www.mpc.edu

Semester system; 6 and 8 week summer sessions; 4 Week Winter Session

Michael Gilmartin, Dean of Instructional Planning

Enrollment: Full-time 1,422 Part-time 6,144

No Housing

OCCUPATIONAL PROGRAMS

Administration of Justice		
Law Enforcement	A	C
Automotive Technology	A	C
Business		
Accounting	A	C
Business Administration	A	C
Entrepreneurship	A	C
General Business	A	C
International Business	A	C
Office Technology	A	C
Secretarial	A	C
Child Development	A	C
Computer Science & Information Systems	A	C
Computer Networking	A	C
Computer Software Applications	A	C
Dental Assisting	A	C
Engineering	A	
Fashion		
Costuming	A	C
Design	A	C
Merchandising	A	C
Production	A	C
Fire Protection Technology	A	C
Fitness Instructor Training	A	C
Graphic Arts	A	C
Hospitality Management	A	
Hospitality Operations	A	C
Human Services	A	C
Interior Design	A	C
Massage Therapy	A	C
Medical Assisting	A	C
Medical Office Administration	A	C
Medical Office Procedures	A	C
Nursing	A	
Ornamental Horticulture	A	C
Parks and Recreation	A	C
Photography	A	C
Physical Education Aide	A	
Pre-Dental Hygiene	A	C
Pre-Occupational Therapy	A	C
Pre-Physical Therapy	A	C
Real Estate	A	C
Restaurant Management	A	
Retail Management		C
Theatre Arts	A	C

A—Associate Degree Program C—Certificate Program

MOORPARK COLLEGE

7075 Campus Rd
Moorpark CA 93021-1695
805-378-1400
805-378-1499 Fax
www.moorparkcollege.edu

Julius Sokenu, Ed. D., Dean Arts, Media, Education & Enrollment Services

Enrollment: Full-time 4,355 Part-time 7,372

Semester system, 4-6-8 week summer session

No Housing

OCCUPATIONAL PROGRAMS

Accounting		C
Biotechnology, General	A	C
Biotechnology, Manufacturing Operators		C
Business	A	C
Business Administration	A	C
Child Development/Early Childhood Education	A	C
Associate Teacher		C
Computer Information Systems, General		C
Computer Networking Systems Engineering (CNSE)	A	C
Advanced Networking Specialist		C
Windows Engineering		C
Computer Science		C
Criminal Justice/Administration of Justice	A	C
Dance	A	C
Engineering	A	C
Environmental Science	A	C
Environmental Studies	A	
Exotic Animal Training and Management	A	C
Film/TV/Media	A	C
Production		C
Studies		C
Graphic Design	A	C
Health Education		C
Health Science		C
Journalism	A	C
Kinesiology	A	C
Exercise Science	A	
Fitness Specialist		C
Intercollegiate Athletics		C
Multimedia	A	C
Music	A	C
Nursing Science	A	C
Nutritional Science		C
Photography	A	C
Commercial		C
Radiologic Technology	A	C
Theater Arts	A	C
Acting	A	C
Directing		C
Technical Theatre	A	C

A—Associate Degree Program C—Certificate Program

MORENO VALLEY COLLEGE

16130 Lasselle St
Moreno Valley CA 92551
951-571-6100
951-571-6176 Fax
www.mvc.edu

Semester system, 6 week summer sessions

Robin Steinback,Ph.D., Vice President of Academic Affairs
Wolde-Ab Isaac, Dean, Health Science Programs

Enrollment: Full-time Part-time

No Housing

OCCUPATIONAL PROGRAMS

Administration of Justice	A	C
AOJ/Basic Correctional Deputy Academy		C
AOJ/Basic Public Safety Dispatch		C
Crime Scene Investigation		C
Investigative Assistant		C
Law Enforcement	A	C
Victim Services Aide		C
Business Administration		
Accounting	A	C
General Business	A	C
Management	A	C
Marketing	A	C
Real Estate	A	C
Small Business Accounting		C
Small Business Payroll Accounting		C
Communications, Media & Languages	A	
Community Interpretation	A	C
Computer Information Systems	A	C
Computer Applications	A	C
Computer Programming	A	C
Simulation and Gaming	A	C
Web Master-Web Designer		C
Web Master-Web Developer		C
Dental Assisting	A	C
Dental Hygiene	A	
Dental Lab Technician	A	C
Early Childhood Education	A	C
Assistant Teacher		C
Early Childhood Intervention Assistant	A	C
Infant and Toddler Specialization		C
Twelve Core Units		C
Education Paraprofessional	A	C
Emergency Medical Services		
Emergency Medical Technician		C
Paramedic	A	C
Fire Technology	A	C
Chief Officer	A	C
Firefight Academy	A	C
Fire Officer	A	C
Human Services	A	C
Employment Support Specialization		C
Kinesiology, Health and Wellness	A	
Medical Assisting		
Admin/Clinical Medical Assisting	A	C
Medical Transcription	A	C
Music	A	
Physician Assistant	A	C

A—Associate Degree Program C—Certificate Program

MT. SAN ANTONIO COLLEGE

1100 N Grand Ave
Walnut CA 91789-1399
909-594-5611
909-468-3955 Fax
www.mtsac.edu

Semester System; 6 Week Summer and Winter Intersessions

Terri Long, Dean of Instructional Services
Dr Irene M Malmgren, Vice President, Instruction

Enrollment: Full-time 8,507 Part-time 15,624

No Housing

OCCUPATIONAL PROGRAMS

Accounting	A	C
Bookkeeping		C
Computerized		C
Financial Planning		C
Managerial		C
Payroll		C
Administrative Assistant	A	
Administrative Assistant Level I, II, III		C
Advertising Design & Illustration	A	
Agri-Technology	A	
Air Conditioning and Refrigeration	A	C
Aircraft Powerplant Maintenance Technology		C
Airframe and Aircraft Powerplant Maintenance Technology	A	
Airframe Maintenance Technology		C
Alcohol/Drug Counseling	A	C
Animation and Gaming	A	
2-D Multimedia		C
3-D and CG Gaming		C
Traditional		C
Architectural Technology Level I	A	C
Design Concentration Level II, III		C
Technology Concentration Level II, III	A	C
Athletic Trainer Aide I		C
Aviation Science	A	
Building Automation		C
Business	A	
Human Resource Management Level I, II, II		C
International Level I, II, III		C
Management Level I, II, III	A	C
Retail Management Level I, II, III	A	C
Small Business Management Level I, II, III		C
Chemical Laboratory Technician	A	
Child Development	A	
Children's Program Certificate		
Administration		C
General Level I, II, III		C
Small Business Management		C
Teaching		C
Coaching		C
Commercial Flight	A	
Communication	A	
Computer and Networking Technology	A	
Computer and Networking Technology Level I and II		C
Computer Graphics Design/Photography		C
Computer Graphics Technology Proficiency		C
Computer Information Systems: Professional Certificate		
C++ Programming		C
C# Programming		C
Database Management Microcomputer		C
Java Programming		C
Linux		C
Networking		C
Network Security		C
Object Oriented Design & Programming		C
Oracle		C
SOA & Web Services		C
SQL		C
Telecommunications		C
Visual Basic Programming		C
Web Programming		C
Windows Operating System Administration		C
Computer Networking Admin. & Security Mgt	A	
Computer Programming	A	
Database Management Systems	A	
Computer Systems Technology		C
Construction Inspection	A	C
Consumer Services		C
Correctional Sciences	A	C
Culinary Arts Level I		C
Dance Teacher		C
Data Entry		C
Digital Photographic Technician		C
Educational Paraprofessional	A	
Educational Paraprofessional: Level I		C
Electronic Assembly and Fabrication		C
Electronic Systems Technology I, II		C
Electronics and Computer Engineering Technology	A	C
Electronics Communications		C
Electronics: Industrial Systems		C
Electronics Technology		C

A—Associate Degree Program C—Certificate Program

MT. SAN ANTONIO COLLEGE (continued)

Emergency Medical Services	A	
Emergency Medical Technician I		C
Emergency Medical Technician: Paramedic		C
Engineering Design Technology Level I, II, III	A	C
Equipment Technology	A	
Escrow Management	A	C
Family and Consumer Sciences	A	
Family Child Care		C
Fashion Design	A	
Fashion Design–Computer Aided		C
Fashion Design Level I, II	A	C
Fashion Merchandising Level I, II	A	C
Fire Technology	A	C
Administration	A	C
Administration Communications	A	
Administration Law	A	
Fire Management	A	C
Fire Prevention	A	
Fire Training	A	
Private Fire Service	A	
Fitness Specialist/Personal Trainer		C
Gallery Design/Operation & Art Profession		C
General Business	A	
Graphic Design and Illustration	A	
Histologic Technician Training	A	
Horse Ranch Management	A	C
Hospitality:		
Catering		C
Food Services		C
Hospitality Management Level I, II		C
Restaurant Management Level I, II		C
Hospitality and Restaurant Management	A	
Human Resources Management	A	
Infant/Toddler Development		C
Information and Operating Systems Security		C
Information Technology	A	
Interior Design	A	
Interior Design – Kitchen and Bath Design	A	
Interior Design Level I: Merchandising		C
Interior Design Level II: Design		C
Interior Design Level III: Professional Designation		C
Interior Landscaping		C
International Business	A	
Introduction to Computer Information Technology		C
Kinesiology and Wellness	A	
Landscape and Park Maintenance		C
Landscape Design and Construction		C
Landscape Equipment Technology		C
Landscape Irrigation		C
Law Enforcement	A	C
Licensed Vocational Nurse to RN	A	
Livestock Management	A	C
LVN (30 Unit Option) Career Mobility Track		C
Machine Operator		C
Manufacturing Technology	A	C
Marketing Management	A	C
MasterCAM		C
Mental Health Technology—		
Psychiatric Technician	A	C
Psychiatric Technician to RN	A	
Microcomputer Productivity Software		C
Music	A	
Nursery Management		C
Nursing	A	
Nutrition Program Assistant:		
Level I		C
Level II Child Program Emphasis		C
Level II Weight Management Program Emphasis		C
Ornamental Horticulture	A	
Paralegal/Legal		
Bankruptcy Specialty	A	
Corporation/Business Specialty	A	
Criminal Specialty	A	
Family Law Specialty	A	
Landlord-Tenant Specialty	A	
Parametric Solid Modeling		C
Park and Sports Turf Management	A	
Park Management		C
Pet Science	A	C
Photography	A	C
Physical Education	A	
Pilates Professional Teacher Training Phase I		C
Programming in C++		C
Programming in Visual Basic		C
Public Works/Landscape Management		C
Radio Broadcasting:		
Behind the Scenes	A	C
On-the-Air	A	C
Radiologic Technology	A	
Real Estate	A	C
Real Estate Appraisal	A	C
Registered Veterinary Technology	A	
Respiratory Therapy	A	
School Age Child—Specialization		C
Sign Language/Interpreting	A	C
Small Business Management	A	C
Sports Turf Management		C
SurfCAM		C
Television Production	A	C
Theater	A	
Tree Care and Maintenance		C
Water Technology		C
Web Page Design		C
Welding	A	C
Automotive Welding, Cutting and Modification		C
Gas Tungston ARC Welding		C
Semiautomatic Welding	A	C

A—Associate Degree Program C—Certificate Program

MT. SAN JACINTO COLLEGE

San Jacinto Campus
1499 N. State St
San Jacinto CA 92583-2399
951-487-6752
951-487-1903 Fax
www.msjc.edu

Semester system, 6 week summer sessions

Patrick Schwerdtfeger, VP of Instruction
Joyce Johnson, Dean of Instruction, Career Technical Education

Enrollment: Full-time 5,153 Part-time 9,538

No Housing

OCCUPATIONAL PROGRAMS

Administration of Justice	A	C
Advanced Audio Technology	A	C
Alcohol and Drug Studies	A	C
ASL-Interpreter Prep Program		C
Audio Technology	A	C
Automotive/Transportation Technology	A	C
Business Administration	A	C
Business Clerical		C
Child Development and Education	A	C
Computer Information Systems (CIS)	A	C
Internet Authoring		C
Networking		C
Programming		C
Diagnostic Medical Sonography	A	
Early Childhood Education	A	
Early Intervention and Inclusion	A	C
Engineering: Drafting Technology	A	C
Fire Technology	A	C
Geographic Information Systems	A	C
Graphic Design	A	
Legal Assistant	A	C
Management/Supervision	A	C
Microsoft Applications		C
Multimedia	A	C
Nursing	A	
Office Administration	A	C
Real Estate	A	C
Small Business Operations		C
Technical Theater	A	C
Turf and Landscape Management	A	C
Water Technology	A	C

A—Associate Degree Program C—Certificate Program

NAPA VALLEY COLLEGE

2277 Napa-Vallejo Hwy
Napa CA 94558-6236
707-253-3000
707-253-3064 Fax
www.napavalley.edu

Faye Smyle, Dean of Instruction

Enrollment: Full-time 2,146 Part-time 4,854

Semester system, 6, 8 week summer session

No Housing

OCCUPATIONAL PROGRAMS

Administration of Justice	A	
911 Dispatcher		C
Addiction Studies		C
Adult Corrections Core Academy		C
Basic Police Academy		C
Juvenile Corrections Core Academy		C
Law Enforcement		C
Probation Officer Core Academy		C
Business Administration		
Accounting	A	
Bookkeeping		C
Business Software		C
Computer Studies	A	
Digital Asset Management		C
Economics		C
Entrepreneurial		C
Office Administration	A	
Child and Family Studies	A	C
Assistant		C
Associate		C
Associate with Administration		C
Master Teacher Specialization		C
Culinary Arts	A	
Digital Design and Graphics Technology	A	C
Emergency Medical Technician: Paramedic	A	
Environmental Science		C
Geographic Information Systems (GIS)		C
Graphic Design	A	
Health Care Programs		
EMT-P: Paramedic		C
Nursing	A	
Psychiatric Technician	A	C
Psychiatric Technician Fast-Track Program		C
Respiratory Care	A	
Vocational Nursing	A	C
Hospitality and Tourism Management	A	C
Human Services		C
Machine Tool Technology	A	C
Music Technology		C
Photography	A	C
Real Estate		C
Viticulture and Winery Technology		C
Viticulture	A	C
Winemaking	A	C
Wine Marketing and Sales	A	C
Web Site Development		C
Welding Technology	A	C

A—Associate Degree Program C—Certificate Program

NORCO COLLEGE

2001 Third St
Norco CA 92860-2600
951- 372-7000
www.norcocollege.edu

Semester system, 6 week summer sessions

Dr. Kevin Fleming, Dean of Instruction, Career and Technical Education

Enrollment: Full-time 3,582 Part-time 7,369

No Housing

OCCUPATIONAL PROGRAMS

Administration of Justice		
Crime Scene Investigation		C
Architectural Graphics		C
Architecture	A	C
Business Administration		
Accounting	A	C
General	A	C
Human Resources	A	C
Logistics Management	A	C
Management	A	C
Marketing	A	C
Real Estate	A	C
Real Estate Salesperson and Transaction		C
Registered and Small Business Income Tax Preparer		C
Small Business Accounting		C
Small Business Payroll Accounting		C
Commercial Music		
Audio Production	A	C
Performance	A	C
Computer Information Systems		
C++ Programming		C
Computer Applications	A	C
Computer Programming	A	C
Desktop Publishing	A	C
Java Programming		C
Mobile Applications Development	A	C
Construction Technology	A	C
Drafting Technology	A	C
Early Childhood Education		
Assistant Teacher		C
Early Childhood Education	A	C
Infant and Toddler Specialization		C
Intervention Assistant	A	C
Twelve Core Units		C
Engineering		
Civil Engineering Technician	A	C
Engineering Graphics		C
Engineering Technology	A	
Green Technician		C
Logistics Management	A	C
Manufacturing Technology		
Automated Systems Technician	A	C
Computer-Aided Production Technology		C
Computer Numerical Control Programming	A	C
Supply Chain Technology	A	C
Retail Management/WAFC	A	C
Simulation & Gaming		
Game Art: 3D Animation	A	C
Game Art: Character Modeling	A	C
Game Art: Core		C
Game Art: Environments and Vehicles	A	C
Game Design	A	C
Game Programming	A	C

A—Associate Degree Program C—Certificate Program

OHLONE COLLEGE

43600 Mission Blvd
Fremont Ca 94539-0390
510-659-6000
510-659-7339 Fax
www.ohlone.edu

Semester system; 6 week summer session

Dr. Leta Stagnaro, Vice President of Academic Affairs

Enrollment: Full-time 3,400 Part-time 7,000

No Housing

OCCUPATIONAL PROGRAMS

3D Modeling and Animation		C
Accounting	A	C
Administration of Justice	A	C
Administrative Assistant with Supervisory Focus	A	C
Biotechnology	A	
Bio-manufacturing		C
Biostatistics		C
Biotechnology Research Associate		C
Broadcasting	A	C
Advanced Film and Video		C
Digital Video and Editing		C
Entertainment Television		C
Live Television Production		C
Radio Air Talent		C
Radio Digital Production		C
Radio Programs Management		C
Radio Studio Operations		C
Sports Television		C
Business Supervision/Management	A	C
Cisco Certified Network Associate		C
Commercial Music		C
Computer Applications in Biotechnology		C
Computer Studies/Internet Web Programming	A	C
Computer Studies/Software Development	A	C
Desktop Support	A	C
Digital Art		C
Engineering/Manufacturing Technician		C
Entertainment Design and Technology		
Audio Technician	A	C
Costuming	A	C
Live Event Management	A	C
Moving Light Technician	A	C
Stage Craft	A	C
Theatrical and TV Lighting Technician	A	C
Fitness Instructor		C
Geographic Information Systems (GIS)		C
Graphic Arts/Computer Graphics	A	C
Graphic Design		C
Interior Design	A	C
Basics		C
Communications		C
Technology		C
Journalism	A	C
Kinesiology		
Athletic Training	A	
Fitness Professional		C
Linux (LPI-1 and LPI-2)		C
Linux/UNIX Administration		C
MCITP Server Administrator		C
Multimedia	A	C
Natural Resource Conservation and Management		C
Network Administrator	A	C
Office Support		C
Photography		C
Physical Therapy Assistant	A	
Real Estate Sales Agent		C
Real Estate Sales Broker	A	C
Real Estate Sales Broker Associate		C
Registered Nurse	A	
Respiratory Therapist	A	
Video Game Development		C

A—Associate Degree Program C—Certificate Program

ORANGE COAST COLLEGE

2701 Fairview Rd
P O Box 5005
Costa Mesa CA 92626
714-432-5072
714-432-5184 Fax
www.orangecoastcollege.edu

16 week Semester System; 6 - 8 Week Summer Session

Kevin Ballinger, Vice President of Instruction

Enrollment: Full-time 12,159 Part-time 24,755

No Housing

OCCUPATIONAL PROGRAMS

Accounting	A	C
Accounting Technician		C
Entry-Level Accounting		C
Full Charge Bookkeeper		C
Architectural Technology		
Architectural Design 1	A	C
Architectural Design 2	A	C
Design/Build		C
Digital Fabrication for Architecture		C
Environmental Recycling & Resource Management		C
Integrated Project Design		C
Sustainable Design		C
Aviation Maintenance Technology		
Airframe	A	C
Airframe and Powerplant	A	C
Avionics		C
Powerplant	A	C
Helicopter Theory and Maintenance		C
Aviation Pilot Training		
Airline Transport Pilot		C
Aviation Science	A	C
Commercial Pilot		C
Flight Operations		C
Instrumental Pilot		C
Private Pilot		C
Business		
Business Administration	A	C
Entrepreneurship		C
Finance		C
Cardiovascular Technology		
Echocardiography and Vascular Ultrasound	A	
Electrocardiography Technician		C
Commercial Art		
Narrative Illustration	A	C
Computer Information Systems		
Business Application Development	A	C
C++ Programming		C
Computer Programming	A	C
Computer Information Systems	A	C
Database Administration (Oracle)		C
Database Developer (Oracle)		C
Enterprise Routing		C
Network Administration & Operations		C
Network Administration-Linux		C
Network Administration-Windows		C
Network Infrastructure		C
Network Professional		C
Network Security		C
Network Services and Applications		C
Network Technician		C
Office Applications		C
Virtualization and Cloud Computing		C
Web Design		C
Construction Technology	A	C
Concrete and Masonry		C
Master Construction Specialist	A	C
Plumbing		C
Residential Construction Development First Award	A	C
Residential Construction Development Second Award		C
Residential Construction Development Third Award		C
Residential Electrical		C
Culinary Arts		C
Advanced Baking and Pastry	A	C
Advanced Culinary Arts	A	C
Baking and Pastry-Basic		C
Culinology® and Food Science		
Culinary Food Science Assistant-Level I		C
Culinology® Level II Professional Level	A	
Dance		
Dance Instructor	A	C
Pilates/Dance Conditioning Instructor		C
World Dance	A	C
Dental Assisting, Registered	A	C
Diagnostic Medical Sonography	A	
Dietetic Technician	A	

A—Associate Degree Program C—Certificate Program

ORANGE COAST COLLEGE (continued)

Digital Media Arts and Design		
Digital Graphics Production	A	C
Graphics Design	A	C
Multimedia	A	C
Display and Visual Presentation	A	C
Early Childhood Education		
Early Childhood Administration	A	C
Early Intervention Aide	A	C
Elementary Teacher/ide	A	C
Family Childcare Provider		C
Infant and Toddler Teacher	A	C
Preschool Teacher	A	C
School-Age Child Care		C
Electronics Technology		
Electro-Mechanical Technician		C
Electronic Reliability Technician		C
Electronics Engineering Technician	A	C
Industrial Automation Technician	A	C
Emergency Medical Services		C
Family and Consumer Sciences	A	
Fashion		
Apparel Construction	A	C
Design	A	C
Fashion Merchandising	A	C
Industrial Sewing		C
Production/Product Development	A	C
Film/Video	A	C
Fitness Specialist	A	C
Food Service Management Commercial (Restaurants/Hotel)		
Catering		C
Quick Service		C
Restaurant	A	
Restaurant Supervision		C
Food Service Management Institutional		
Dietetic Service Manager		C
Dietetic Service Supervisor		C
Dietetic Technician–Management Health Care	A	
Heating, Ventilation, Air Conditioning & Refrigeration Technology	A	C
Hospitality, Travel & Tourism Airline & Travel Careers	A	C
Airline Travel Careers	A	C
Corporate/Contract Flight Attendant		C
Spa Management		C
Horticulture	A	C
Hotel Management		
Front Office Specialist		C
Human Resource Management	A	C
Meeting and Event Management		C
Room Operations Specialist	A	C
Sales and Marketing Specialist	A	C
Interior Design		
Interior Design Assistant-Level I		C
Interior Design–Professional Level III		C
Interior Merchandising-Level I		C
Kitchen and Bath–Advanced		C
Management		
Management and Leadership Studies	A	C
Management Institute		C
Retail	A	C
Manufacturing Technology		
CNC Machine Operator	A	C
CNC Machine Programmer	A	C
CNC Operator		C
CNC Programmer		C
Machinist	A	C
Tooling	A	C
Marketing (Merchandising)		
Advertising		C
Entry Level Marketing		C
General Marketing	A	C
International Business	A	C
Sales		C
Medical Assisting/CMA Eligible Program	A	C
Mental Health Worker	A	C
Music		
Business Employee	A	C
MIDI Applications	A	C
Musical Entertainer–Instrumental	A	C
Musical Entertainer–Vocal	A	C
Studio Guitar Performer	A	C
Neurodiagnostic Technology	A	
Nutrition Careers		
Nutrition and Fitness Education		C
Nutrition Education	A	C
Photography		
Digital SLR Photography and Videography		C
Digital Technician		C
Still	A	C
Polysomnographic	A	
Neurodiagnostic Technology Option	A	
Polysomnographic Technology	A	
Professional Mariner-Level 1		C
Radiologic Technology (Diagnostics)	A	
Real Estate		
Broker	A	C
Salesperson		C
Respiratory Care	A	
Speech-Language Pathology Assistant	A	
Tourism		
Cruise Specialist		C
Destination Management		C
Travel Agency Specialist		C
Travel and Tourism	A	
Tour Escorting and Management		C
Welding Technology	A	C
Advanced II Welding (FCAW)		C
Advanced Welding (FCAW)		C
Advanced Welding (SMAW)		C

A—Associate Degree Program C—Certificate Program

ORANGE COAST COLLEGE (continued)

Basic Welding (SMAW)	C
Gas Metal Arc Welding (GMAW)	C
Gas Tungsten Arc Welding (GTAW)	C
Intermediate Welding (SMAW)	C
Orbital	C
Pipe	C

OXNARD COLLEGE

4000 S Rose Ave
Oxnard CA 93033-6699
805-986-5800
805-986-5865 Fax
www.oxnardcollege.edu

Ms. Carmen Guerrero, Dean of Career and Technical Education

Enrollment: Full-time 3,900 Part-time 3,700

Semester system (16 Weeks); 4 and 6 week summer sessions

No Housing

OCCUPATIONAL PROGRAMS

Accounting		C
Addictive Disorders Studies	A	C
Alcohol/Drug Counselors	A	C
Criminal Justice System	A	C
American Sign Language		C
Deaf Studies	A	
Assistive Computer Technology		C
Automotive		
Automotive Body and Fender Repair	A	C
Automotive Technology	A	C
Business		
Business	A	C
Business Administration	A	C
Management	A	C
Child Development	A	C
Coastal Environmental Studies	A	
Communication Studies	A	C
Computer Applications and Office Technologies		
Administrative Assistant	A	C
Computer Information Systems		C
Computer Networking	A	C
Culinary Arts and Restaurant Management		
Culinary Arts	A	C
Restaurant Management	A	C
Dance		C
Dental Assisting	A	C
Dental Hygiene	A	C
Digital Media Studies		C
Early Childhood Education	A	C
Emergency Medical Technician		C
Refresher		C
Environmental Control Technologies	A	C
Fire Technology		
Extended Fire Technology Education		C
Fire Technology (Pre-Service)	A	C
Geology		C
Kinesiology	A	
Marine Studies		C
Music		C
Paralegal Studies	A	C
TV, Filmmaking, and Media Art	A	C

A—Associate Degree Program C—Certificate Program

PALOMAR COLLEGE

1140 W Mission Rd
San Marcos CA 92069-1487
760-744-1150
760-591-9108 Fax
www.palomar.edu

Wilma Owens, Dean of Career, Technical and Extended Education

Enrollment: 27,026

Semester system; 6 and 8 week summer sessions

No Housing

OCCUPATIONAL PROGRAMS

Program		
Administration of Justice		
Basic Police Academy		C
General	A	
Homeland Security	A	
Investigations	A	
Law Enforcement	A	
Art		
Graphic Design	A	
Illustration	A	
Interactive Media Design	A	C
Automotive Technology		
Auto Chassis and Drive Lines	A	C
Auto Collision Repair	A	C
Diesel Technology	A	C
Electronic Tune-Up and Computer Control Systems	A	C
Mechanics - General	A	C
Aviation Sciences		
Aircraft Commercial Pilot	A	C
Aviation Operations and Management	A	C
Business		
Accounting	A	C
Administrative Assistant	A	C
Advertising, Marketing, and Merchandising	A	C
Business Administration	A	
Business - General	A	
Business Management	A	C
E-Marketing	A	C
International Business	A	C
Legal Studies	A	
Medical Office Specialist	A	C
Real Estate		
Broker License Preparation	A	C
Escrow	A	C
Retail Management		C
Cabinet and Furniture Technology		
Cabinetmaking and Furniture Design	A	C
Cabinetmaking and Millwork	A	C
Furniture Making	A	C
Child Development		
Child and Family Services	A	C
Early Childhood Administration	A	C
Early Inclusion Teacher	A	C
Infant/Toddler Teacher	A	C
Preschool teacher	A	C
Computer Science & Information Systems		
Computer Network Administration	A	C
Computer Science	A	C
Computer Science with Emphasis in Video Gaming	A	C
Information Technology	A	C
Construction Technology and Management		
Construction Inspection	A	C
Dance	A	C
Dental Assisting		
Dental Assisting (Registered Dental Assisting)	A	C
Digital Broadcast Arts	A	C
Digital Video	A	C
Entertainment Technology		C
Radio and Television	A	C
Drafting Technology		
Computer Assisted Drafting	A	C
Drafting Technology - Multimedia	A	C
Drafting Technology - Technical	A	C
Electro-Mechanical Drafting and Design	A	C
Interactive Media Design	A	C
Emergency Medical Education		
Paramedic Training	A	C
Family and Consumer Sciences-General	A	C
Fashion		
Fashion Buying and Management	A	
Fashion Design, Technical	A	
Fashion Merchandising	A	C
Fire Technology	A	C
Graphic Communications–Imaging & Publishing		
Digital Imaging	A	C
Graphic Communications –Emphasis in Digital Distribution	A	C
Graphic Communications–Emphasis in Management	A	C
Graphic Communications–Emphasis in Production	A	C
Screen Printing	A	C

A—Associate Degree Program C—Certificate Program

PALOMAR COLLEGE (continued)

Graphic Communications–Multimedia & Web		
Digital Video	A	C
Interactive Media Design		
Emphasis in 3D Modeling and Animation	A	C
Emphasis in Multimedia Design	A	C
Interactive Web Multimedia and Audio	A	C
Internet		
Emphasis in Graphic Communication	A	C
New Media Compositing, Authoring and Distribution	A	C
Interior Design	A	C
Journalism	A	C
Kinesiology	A	
Adult Fitness/Health Management		C
Library Technology	A	C
Nursing Education		
Associate Degree Nursing Curriculum (2 years)	A	
Associate Degree Nursing Curriculum (LVN to RN)	A	
Associate Degree Nursing (RN) Advanced Standing By Transfer	A	
Associate Degree Nursing (RN) Advanced Standing for LVN's By Completion of an LVN-RN Transition Course	A	
Nursing - Associate Degree Nursing (RN to ADN)	A	
Photography	A	C
Digital Imaging	A	C
Psychology		
Alcohol and Other Drug Studies	A	C
Psychological and Social Services	A	C
Public Administration	A	C
Public Works Management	A	C
Recreation		
Outdoor Leadership	A	C
Recreation Agency Leader	A	C
Sign Language, American		
English Interpreter Training Program	A	C
Theater Arts	A	
Entertainment Technology		C
Theatre Arts	A	
Theatre–Technical		C
Wastewater Technology Education	A	C
Water Technology Education	A	C
Welding Technology	A	C

A—Associate Degree Program C—Certificate Program

PALO VERDE COLLEGE

1 College Blvd
Blythe CA 92225-1199
760-921-5500
www.paloverde.edu

Sean C. Hancock, Vice President, Instruction and Student Services

Enrollment: Full-time 249 Part-time 2,580

Semester System

No Housing

OCCUPATIONAL PROGRAMS

ADS Specialist I, II		C
Agricultural Crop Science		C
Alcohol and Drug Studies		C
Automotive Technology	A	C
Fabrication		C
Building Construction Technology	A	C
Business Management	A	C
Business Literacy		C
Personal Finance		C
Small Business Management		C
Child Development	A	C
Assistant		C
Associate Teacher		C
Teacher		C
Computer Information Systems	A	
3 D Computer Animation		C
Computer Applications		C
Graphic Design and Web Content		C
Information Technology Literacy		C
Management Information Systems		C
Criminal Justice	A	C
Fire Science Technology		
Firefighter I		C
Fire Instructor I, II		C
Hazardous Material Specialist	A	C
Nurse and Allied Health		
Certified Nursing Assistant		C
Emergency Medical Technician		C
Traditional Vocational Nursing		C
Phlebotomy		C
Welding Technology	A	C

A—Associate Degree Program C—Certificate Program

PASADENA CITY COLLEGE

1570 E Colorado Blvd
Pasadena CA 91106-2003
626-585-7123
626-585-7923 Fax
www.pasadena.edu

Two 16 week semesters; Winter and summer intersessions

Salomón Dávila, Dean, Economic and Workforce Development

Enrollment: Full-time and Part-time 29,000

No Housing

OCCUPATIONAL PROGRAMS

Accounting - Bookkeeping	A	C
Accounting-Bookkeeping Assistant	A	C
Accounting Clerk	A	C
Administration of Justice	A	C
Architecture	A	
Automotive Technology		
Air Conditioning Technician	A	C
All Automotive Systems	A	C
Electrical/Electronics Systems		C
Engine Performance Technician	A	C
Powertrain Technician	A	C
Undercar Technician	A	C
Underhood Technician	A	C
Biologic Technology	A	C
Computational Biology		C
Laboratory Assistant	A	C
Stem Cell Culture		C
Building Construction	A	C
Business Administration		
Entrepreneurship	A	C
Financial Investment	A	C
International Business/Trade	A	C
Management	A	C
Marketing Merchandising	A	C
Retail Management	A	C
Business Information Technology	A	C
Administrative Assistant	A	C
Business Software Specialist	A	C
Information and Records Specialist	A	C
Child Development	A	C
Communication Arts	A	
Computer Information Systems		
Microcomputer Support	A	C
Operations	A	C
Programming	A	C
Small Computer Applications	A	C
Construction Inspection	A	C
Cosmetology		
Cosmetology	A	C
Instructional Techniques in Cosmetology	A	C
Culinary Arts		C

Dental Assisting	A	C
Dental Hygiene	A	C
Dental Laboratory Technology	A	C
Digital Media		
Computer Assisted Photo Imaging	A	C
Foundation	A	C
Graphic Design	A	C
Web Design and Development	A	C
Early Childhood Education	A	
Electrical Technology	A	C
Basic Photovoltaic Design and Installation	A	C
Engineering Design Technology—CAD/CAM Technician	A	C
Fashion		
Assistant	A	C
Design	A	C
Fire Technology	A	C
Graphic Communications Technology		
Computer Imaging and Composition	A	C
Screen Printing	A	C
Hospitality Management	A	C
Interior Design	A	C
Journalism		
Photojournalism	A	C
Printed Media	A	C
Kinesiology and Wellness	A	
Library Technology	A	C
Machine Shop Technology	A	C
Medical Assisting		
Administrative-Clinical	A	C
Medical Office—Administrative	A	C
Medical Office Insurance Biller	A	C
Music	A	
Nursing		
Anesthesia Technician	A	C
LVN	A	
Registered	A	C
Vocational	A	C
Paralegal Studies	A	C
Photography	A	C
Post-Production	A	C

A—Associate Degree Program C—Certificate Program

PASADENA CITY COLLEGE (continued)

Product Design Programs		
Graphics	A	C
Technology	A	C
Radiologic Technology	A	C
Speech/Language Pathology Assistant	A	
Television and Radio	A	C
Audio Production		C
Broadcast Journalism	A	C
Television Operations	A	C
Television Production		C
Theater Arts	A	C
Theater Technology	A	C
Welding	A	C
Construction Welding	A	C
Gas Tungsten and Gas Metal Welding	A	C

A—Associate Degree Program C—Certificate Program

PORTERVILLE COLLEGE

100 E College Ave
Porterville CA 93257-5901
559-791-2200
559-791-2408 Fax
www.portervillecollege.edu

Semester system; 16 week fall, spring semester; 6 week summer session

Bill Henry, Vice President, Academic Affairs

Enrollment: Full-time 1,823 Part-time 2,583

No Housing

OCCUPATIONAL PROGRAMS

Administration of Justice (AS-T)	A	C
Agriculture Production	A	
Business	A	
Business Administration (AS-T)	A	
Child Development	A	
Child Development Associate Teacher		C
Child Development Teacher		C
Emergency Medical Technician, (Job Skills)		C
Entrepreneurship		C
Fire Technology		C
Human Services		C
Industrial Maintenance Technology		C
Industrial Technology (Job Skills)		C
Information Systems	A	C
LVN to Associate Degree Nursing	A	
Nursing	A	
Power Technician/Utility Worker		C
Psychiatric Technology		C
Solar Sales (Job Skills)		C
Vocational Nurse		C
Wildland Fire Fighter Academy (Job Skills)		C

A—Associate Degree Program C—Certificate Program

COLLEGE OF THE REDWOODS

7351 Tompkins Hill Rd
Eureka CA 95501-9300
707-476-4100
707-476-4400 Fax
www.redwoods.edu

Marla Gleave, Dean, Career and Technical Education

Enrollment: Full-time 2,328 Part-time 3,884

Semester system; 6, 8 & 12 week summer sessions

Dormitories

OCCUPATIONAL PROGRAMS

Addiction Studies		C
Administration of Justice	A	C
Basic Law Enforcement Academy		C
Corrections Officer		C
Probation Officer		C
Agriculture	A	
Automotive Technology	A	
Advanced Automotive Technology		C
Basic Automotive Technology		C
Business		
Bookkeeping		C
General Business	A	C
Payroll Clerk		C
Computer Information Systems		
CIS Networking	A	C
Construction Technology	A	
Cabinetmaking and Millwork		C
Fine Woodworking I		C
Fine Woodworking II		C
Residential Construction I		C
Residential Construction II		C
Residential Wiring		C
Solar Photovoltaic Technician		C
Solar Thermal Technician		C
Dental Assisting	A	C
Digital Media	A	C
Drafting Technology		
Architectural Drafting	A	C
Civil Design	A	C
Mechanical Drafting	A	C
Early Childhood Education	A	C
Forest and Natural Resources Technology	A	
Forestry Technology		C
Geomatics		C
Hotel/Restaurant/Culinary (HRC)		
Hospitality Management	A	C
Restaurant Management	A	C
Manufacturing Technology	A	C
CAD/CAM Design and Manufacturing	A	C
Manufacturing Technology		
CADD/CAM Manufacturing	A	C
Nursing		
LVN	A	C
LVN to RN	A	C
RN	A	
Welding Technology	A	
Electric Arc and Oxyacetylene Welding		C
MIG and TIG Welding		C

A—Associate Degree Program C—Certificate Program

REEDLEY COLLEGE

995 N Reed Ave
Reedley CA 93654-2099
559-638-3641
559-638-0305 Fax
www.reedleycollege.edu

18 week semester system, 6 week summer sessions

Marie Byrd-Harris, Interim, Dean of Instruction

Enrollment: Full-time 5,300 Part-time 4,078

Dormitories for Men; Dormitories for Women

OCCUPATIONAL PROGRAMS

Accounting	A	C
Accounting Assistant		C
Accounting Intern		C
Agriculture Business	A	C
Agriculture-General	A	
Airframe		C
Animal Science	A	
Arboriculture		C
Associate Teacher		C
Automotive Technician Program	A	C
Aviation Maintenance Technology	A	
Airframe		C
Aviation Maintenance Technology		C
Powerplant		C
Business Administration		
Business Intern		C
Hospitality Management		C
Managerial Assistant		C
Retailing	A	
Small Business Management	A	C
Call Center Clerk		C
Child Development	A	C
Child Care for School-Age Children/Associate Teacher		C
Child Care for School-Age Children/Teacher		C
Early Intervention Assistant		C
Paraprofessional-48 and 60 Unit Option		C
Coaching		C
Computer Animation		C
Computer Digital Imaging		C
Computer Science	A	
Criminology		
Corrections	A	C
Law Enforcement	A	C
Customer Service		C
Dental Assisting	A	C
Entrepreneur		C
Environmental Horticulture	A	C
Environmental Horticulture, Maintenance		C
Family Child Care		C
File Clerk		C
Floral Design		C
Foods and Nutrition	A	C
Forest/Park Technology	A	
Forestry Technician Firefighter Emphasis		C
Forest Surveying Technology		C
Forest Technology		C
General Office Secretarial	A	C
Graphic Design		C
Health Care Interpreter		C
Human Services		C
Infant/Toddler		C
Information Systems	A	C
Help Desk		C
Networking		C
Programming for the Web		C
Web Design	A	C
Manufacturing		
Machinist Certificate		C
Welder		C
Machine Shop Turning and Milling		C
Machine Tool	A	C
Maintenance Mechanic		C
Management	A	
Entry Level		C
Mechanized Agriculture	A	C
Medical Administrative Assistant	A	
Metal Working		C
Music		
Instrumental	A	
Vocal	A	
Natural Resources		
Forestry Technician Firefighting Emphasis		C
Forest Surveying Technology		C
Forest Technology		C
Recreation and Interpretation Techniques		C
Training and Applied Work Experience		C
Nursing		
LVN		C
Nursing Assistant Training		C
RN		C

A—Associate Degree Program C—Certificate Program

REEDLEY COLLEGE continued

Office Technology	A	C
Administrative Assistant		C
Office Assistant		C
Office Secretarial–General	A	C
Plant and Soil Science	A	C
Irrigation/Fertility Technician		C
Receptionist	A	C
Sport Turf Management		C
Web Design	A	C
Web–Programming		C
Welding	A	C
Welding–Advanced		C
Word Processing	A	C

A—Associate Degree Program C—Certificate Program

RIO HONDO COLLEGE

3600 Workman Mill Rd
Whittier CA 90601-1616
562-692-0921
562-699-7386 Fax
www.riohondo.edu

Mike Slavich, Dean of Career and Technical Eduction

Enrollment: Full-time 4,646 Part-time 13,395

Semester system; summer sessions available

No Housing

OCCUPATIONAL PROGRAMS

Accounting	A	C
Computerized		C
Accounting for Government and Non-Profit Organizations		C
Administration of Justice	A	
Alternative Energy Technology	A	C
Alternative Fuels/Advanced Transportation Technology	A	C
Animation	A	
Architectural	A	
Architectural Design and Drawing	A	
Architectural Design and Drawing Technician		C
Art–Commercial	A	
Athletic Trainer's Aide		C
Automotive Technology	A	
Advanced Engine Performance	A	C
Advanced Engine Performance Technician		C
Brake and Suspension Services		C
Collision Repair & Painting	A	C
Diesel Fuel and Emission Systems		C
Engine Repair		C
Fuel Injection Systems		C
General Automotive Service		C
General Service Technician		C
Honda/Acura Air Conditioning and Supplemental Restraint Systems		C
Honda/Acura Brakes, Suspension, and Electronic Systems		C
Honda/Acura Engine Repair and Chassis Electrical Systems		C
Honda/Acura Power Train and Transmission Systems		C
Honda Professional Career Training Program Specialization	A	
Safety, Comfort and Convenience Systems		C
Transmission Service		C
Basic Police Training		C
Business Administration	A	
Business Management/Supervision	A	C
Business Marketing	A	C
Child Development	A	C
Preschool Teacher		C
Civil Design Technology	A	C
Civil Design and Drawing		C
Computer Information Technology (CIT)		
Computer Systems	A	C
Microcomputer Specialist	A	C
Computer Information Technology Systems	A	C
Corrections	A	
Early Childhood Education	A	C
Electronics Technology	A	C
Emergency Medical Technician (EMT)		C
Engineering Design and Drafting	A	
Technician		C
Environmental Science	A	
Environmental Technology	A	C
Fire Technology	A	C
Fitness Specialist		C
Game Development		C
Geographical Information System (GIS)		C
Heavy Equipment Technology	A	C
Home Health Aide		C
Human Services		C
Income Tax Preparer		C
International Business	A	C
Logistics Management	A	C
Mass Communications		
Mass Media Specialization	A	C
Print Media Specialization	A	C
Nursing		
ADN (RN)	A	
Assistant Pre-Certification Training Course		C
Certified Nurse Assistant Acute Care		C
LVN to ADN	A	
Psy Tech to RN	A	
Vocational		C
Photography	A	
Retail Management		C
Small Business/Entrepreneurialism	A	C
Surveying, Mapping and Drawing		C
Theatre Arts	A	
Welding Technology	A	C
Wildland Fire Technology	A	C

A—Associate Degree Program C—Certificate Program

RIVERSIDE CITY COLLEGE

4800 Magnolia Ave
Riverside CA 92506-1299
951-222-8490
951-222-8623 Fax
www.rcc.edu

Susan Mills, Vice President, Career Technology Programs

Enrollment: 33,000

Semester system; 6 week summer intersession, 6 week winter intersession

No Housing

OCCUPATIONAL PROGRAMS

Administration of Justice	A	C
Investigative Assistant		C
Crime Scene Investigation		C
Victim Services Aide		C
Air Conditioning and Refrigeration	A	C
Applied Digital Media and Printing	A	C
Basic Electronic Prepress		C
Basic Graphic Design		C
New Media and Interactive Design		C
Art		
Visual Communications-Animation		C
Visual Communications-Illustration		C
Automotive Technology		
Automotive Body Repair	A	C
Automotive Trim & Upholstery	A	C
Electrical	A	C
Ford Specialty	A	
General Motors Specialty	A	
Mechanical	A	C
Bank Operations		C
Business Administration	A	C
Accounting Concentration	A	C
Banking and Finance Concentration	A	C
General Business Concentration	A	C
Human Resources Concentration	A	C
Insurance	A	C
International Business		C
Management Concentration	A	C
Marketing Concentration	A	C
Operations and Production Management		C
Real Estate Concentration	A	C
Computer Applications & Office Technology		
Administrative Office Professional		C
Executive Office Management	A	C
Executive Office Professional		C
Legal Administrative Professional		C
Office Assistant		C
Office Fast-Track		C
Virtual Assistant		C

Computer Information Systems		
C++ Programming		C
CISCO Networking		C
Computer Applications	A	C
Computer Programming	A	C
E-commerce		C
Java Programming		C
Relational Database Management Tech		C
Systems Development		C
Webmaster-Web Designer		C
Webmaster-Web Developer		C
Cosmetology	A	C
Cosmetology Business Administration, Entrepreneurial Concentration	A	C
Cosmetology Business Administration, Management and Supervision Concentration	A	C
Cosmetology Instructor Training		C
Esthetician		C
Culinary Arts	A	C
Dance		
Pilates Dance/Conditioning Instructor		C
Early Childhood Education	A	C
Assistant Teacher		C
Early Childhood Intervention Assistant	A	C
Infant and Toddler Specialization		C
Twelve Core Units		C
Educational Paraprofessional	A	C
Film Television and Video		
Basic Televison Production		C
Production Specialist	A	C
Human Services	A	C
Employment Support Specialization		C
Kinesiology/Exercise, Sport and Wellness		
Athletic Training Emphasis	A	C
Coaching Emphasis	A	C
Fitness Professions Emphasis	A	C
Music	A	
Jazz Performance		C
Music Technology		C
Music Performance		C
Piano Performance		C

A—Associate Degree Program   C—Certificate Program

RIVERSIDE CITY COLLEGE (continued)

Nursing		
Critical Care Nurse		C
Nursing Assistant		C
Registered Nursing	A	
Vocational Nursing	A	C
Paralegal Studies	A	
Photography	A	C
Retail Management/WAFC	A	C
Sign Language Interpreting	A	C
Welding Technology	A	C
Stick (SMAW)		C
Tig (TGAW)		C
Wire (FCAW, GMAW)		C

A—Associate Degree Program C—Certificate Program

SACRAMENTO CITY COLLEGE

3835 Freeport Blvd
Sacramento CA 95822-1386
916-558-2568
916-558-2098 Fax
www.scc.losrios.edu

Gabriel Meehan, Associate Vice President of Instruction, Economic and Workforce Development

Enrollment: 25,000

Semester system; 4, 6 and 8 week summer sessions

No Housing

OCCUPATIONAL PROGRAMS

Accounting	A	
Clerk		C
Full Charge Bookkeeper		C
Administration of Justice	A	
Aeronautics		
Aircraft Dispatcher	A	C
Airframe	A	C
Air Traffic Control	A	
Combined Airframe and Powerplant	A	C
Flight Technology	A	C
Powerplant	A	C
Biology, Field Ecology		C
Business	A	C
Accounting	A	
Accounting Clerk		C
Customer Service		C
Full Charge Bookkeeper		C
General	A	
Management	A	C
Marketing, Advertising	A	C
Office Administration	A	C
Business Operations and Management Technology, Level C		C
Clerical General Office, Level A		C
Computer Keyboarding and Office Application		C
Introduction to Computerized Office Technologies, Level B		C
Virtual Offices and Management Technologies, Level D	A	C
Real Estate	A	C
Retail Management		C
Small Business Management	A	C
Chemistry, Chemical Technician	A	C
Computer Information Science	A	C
Advanced CISCO Networking		C
Computer Science	A	C
Information Processing	A	
Information Systems Security	A	C
Management Information Science	A	C
Network Administration	A	C
Network Design	A	C
PC Support		C
Programming		C
Web Developer	A	C
Web Professional		C
Webmaster Level 1		C
Webmaster Level 2		C
Word Processing Technician		C
Cosmetology	A	C
Art and Science of Nail Technology		C
Dental Assisting	A	C
Dental Hygiene	A	
Early Childhood Education	A	C
Administration	A	
Child Development	A	
Family Child Care		C
Infant Care and Education Teacher		C
School-Age Care and Education Teacher		C
Teacher	A	
Electronics Technology		
Automated Systems Technician	A	C
Electronics Facilities Maintenance Technician	A	C
Electronics Mechanic		C
Microcomputer Technician	A	C
Telecommunications Technician	A	C
Engineering Design Technology	A	C
Architectural/Structural Drafting	A	C
Electric (Power-Lighting Systems)	A	C
Engineering Design Technology	A	
HVAC Systems Design	A	C
Mechanical (HVAC/Plumbing Systems)	A	C
Surveying (Geomatics)		C
Family and Consumer Science	A	
Instructional Assisting, Bilingual/Bicultural Emphasis	A	C
Instructional Assisting, General	A	C
Instructional Assisting, Special Education	A	C
Fashion		
Applied Apparel Studies Construction		C
Applied Apparel Studies Production	A	
Custom Apparel Construction and Alterations	A	C
Fashion Design and Production		C

A—Associate Degree Program C—Certificate Program

SACRAMENTO CITY COLLEGE (continued)

Graphic Communication	A	C
3D Animation and Modeling		C
Game Design		C
Graphic Design		C
Interactive Design		C
Web Design		C
Journalism	A	
Multimedia News Specialist		C
Visual Journalism		C
Kinesiology		
Athletic Coaching Certification		C
Fitness Instructor Certification		C
Library and Information Technology	A	C
Mechanical-Electrical Technology	A	C
Commercial Building Energy Auditing and Commissioning Specialist		C
Electrical Technology		C
Mechanical Systems Technician		C
Music, Commercial		
Audio Production Emphasis	A	C
Music Business Management Emphasis	A	C
General	A	
Performance Emphasis	A	C
Songwriting/Arranging Emphasis	A	C
Nursing		
30 Unit Option		C
Registered	A	
Vocational	A	C
Occupational Therapy Assistant	A	
Photography	A	C
Commercial and Magazine Photography		C
Portrait and Wedding Photography		C
Visual Journalism		C
Physical Therapist Assistant	A	
Railroad Operations	A	C
Theatre Arts		
Acting-Directing Emphasis	A	
Film Production		C
Technical Production Emphasis	A	

A—Associate Degree Program C—Certificate Program

SADDLEBACK COLLEGE

28000 Marguerite Pkwy
Mission Viejo CA 92692
949-582-4500
949-347-0438 Fax
www.saddleback.edu

Semester System; 6 and 8 Week Summer Session

Kathy Werle, Vice President of Instruction

Enrollment: Full-time 7,835 Part-time 17,304

No Housing

OCCUPATIONAL PROGRAMS

Program	A	C
Accounting		
Accountant	A	C
Computerized Accounting Specialist	A	C
Tax Preparation	A	C
Administrative Assistant	A	C
American Sign Language Interpreting	A	C
Architectural Drafting	A	C
Automotive Technology		
Alternative Fuel Vehicle Specialist	A	C
Automotive Chassis Specialist	A	C
Automotive Engine Performance Specialist	A	C
Automotive Engine Service Specialist	A	C
General Automotive Technician	A	C
Business		
Administration	A	
Entrepreneurship	A	C
Global Business	A	C
Leadership	A	C
Management	A	
Marketing	A	C
Professional Retailing	A	C
Retail Management	A	C
Child Development and Education		
Early Childhood Teacher	A	C
Early Interventionist	A	C
Infant Toddler Teacher	A	C
Master Teacher	A	C
School Age Care and Recreation	A	C
Site Supervisor	A	C
Cinema/TV/Radio	A	C
Cinema	A	C
CTVR-Critical Studies	A	C
Post Production	A	C
Radio	A	C
Television	A	C
Screen Acting and Voice Performance	A	C
Computer Information Management		
Applications Developer	A	C
E-Commerce Specialist	A	C
Network Administrator	A	C
Software Specialist	A	C
Web Designer	A	C
Webmaster	A	C
Computer Maintenance Technology	A	C
Construction Inspection	A	C
Consumer Services	A	C
Cosmetology		C
Culinary Arts		
Advanced Culinary Arts	A	C
Basic Culinary Arts	A	C
Catering	A	C
Drafting Technology		C
Ecological Restoration		C
Electronic Technology		
Analog and Digital Circuit/ Electronic Technology	A	C
Digital Electronic Technology	A	C
General Electronic Technology	A	C
Engineering	A	
Environmental Studies	A	
Family and Consumer Sciences	A	C
Fashion Design		
Advanced Fashion Design and Apparel Mfg.	A	C
Fashion Design	A	C
Fashion Merchandising		
Fashion Merchandising	A	C
Visual Fashion Merchandising	A	C
Gerontology		C
Graphics		
Computer Graphics	A	C
Graphic Communications	A	C
Graphic Design	A	C
Illustration/Animation	A	C
Health Information Technology	A	C
Horticulture	A	C
Human Services		
Alcohol and Drug Studies	A	C
Community-Based Corrections	A	C
Human Services Generalist	A	C
Mental Health Worker	A	C

A—Associate Degree Program C—Certificate Program

SADDLEBACK COLLEGE (continued)

Interior Design		
Interior Design Assistant		C
Interior Design Professional	A	C
Interiors Merchandising		C
Journalism	A	C
Landscape Design	A	C
Marine Science Technology		
Marine Science Technician	A	C
Seamanship	A	C
Medical Assistant		
Administrative Medical Assistant		C
Clinical Medical Assistant		C
Comprehensive Medical Assistant		C
Medical Lab Technology	A	C
Nursing		
LVN to RN Advanced Placement Option		C
Registered Nurse	A	C
Nutrition	A	C
Paramedic	A	C
Photography	A	
Rapid Digital Manufacturing	A	C
Real Estate		
Real Estate Appraisal	A	C
Real Estate Escrow	A	C
Real Estate Sales/Broker	A	C
Theatre Arts		
Entertainment and Theatre Technology		C
Performance and Acting	A	
Technical Theatre	A	
Travel and Tourism	A	C

A—Associate Degree Program C—Certificate Program

SAN BERNARDINO VALLEY COLLEGE

701 S Mount Vernon Ave
San Bernardino CA 92410
909-384-4400
909-384-5485 Fax
www.valleycollege.edu

Semester system; 6 week summer sessions

Dr. Kay Ragan, Dean, Career and Technical Education

Enrollment: Full-time 2,760 Part-time 9,240

No Housing

OCCUPATIONAL PROGRAMS

Program	A	C
Accounting	A	C
Bookkeeping		C
Administration of Justice	A	C
Aeronautics		
Airframe Maintenance Technician		C
Aviation Maintenance Technician	A	C
Avionics Technology	A	C
Powerplant Maintenance Technician		C
Architecture & Environmental Design	A	
Computer Aided Drafting Technician		C
Art	A	
Graphic Design	A	C
Web and Multimedia Design		C
Automotive Technology		
Advanced Automotive Body & Paint	A	C
Automatic Transmission Technology	A	C
Automotive Technician	A	C
Basic Automotive Body and Paint	A	C
Engine Performance		C
Wheel Alignment and Brakes	A	C
Business Administration	A	C
Retail Management		C
Child Development	A	
Associate Teacher		C
Family Child Care		C
Infant Development		C
Master Teacher		C
School-Age		C
Site Supervisor		C
Teacher		C
Computer Information Technology (CIT)	A	C
Administrative Assistant	A	C
Cisco Certified Network Associate		C
Office/Clerical		C
Computer Science	A	C
Corrections		C
Culinary Arts	A	C
Dining Room Service		C
Food Preparation		C
Food Service		C
Diesel		
Heavy-Duty Diesel Technician		C
Electricity/Electronics		
Avionics Technology	A	C
Communications Engineering Technology	A	C
Computer Engineering Technology	A	C
Electric Power Technology	A	C
Electronics Technology	A	C
General Electrician		C
Foods and Nutrition	A	C
Dietetic Aide		C
Dietetic Service Supervisor		C
Geographic Information Systems (GIS)		C
Human Services	A	C
Alcohol/Drug Studies		C
Career Specialist		C
Case Management		C
Inspection Technology	A	C
Library Technology	A	C
Nursing	A	
Pharmacy Technology	A	C
Psychiatric Technology	A	C
Radio, Television & Film		
Digital Film Production		C
Film	A	C
Radio	A	C
Television	A	C
Refrigeration and Air Conditioning	A	C
Water Supply Technology	A	C
Water Distribution		C
Water Treatment		C
Welding Technology		
Consolidated Welding	A	C
General Welding	A	C
Shielded Metal Arc Welding (SMAW)		C
Welding Inspection Technology		C

A—Associate Degree Program C—Certificate Program

SAN DIEGO CITY COLLEGE

1313 Park Blvd
San Diego CA 92101-4787
619-388-3400
619-388-3165 Fax
www.sdcity.edu

Randy Barnes, Vice President of Instruction

Enrollment: Full-time & Part-time 14,000

Semester system

No Housing

OCCUPATIONAL PROGRAMS

Program		
Air Conditioning, Refrigeration, and Environmental Control Technology	A	
A/C, Heating and Advanced Refrigeration		C
Advanced A/C and Direct Digital Control		C
Basic Refrigeration and Control Systems		C
Heating, A/C and Solar Energy		C
Stationary Facilities Engineering and General Maintenance Technician		C
Agriculture		
Sustainable Urban Agriculture	A	C
Alcohol and Other Drug Studies	A	C
Biotechnology	A	C
Business Studies		
Real Estate	A	
Real Estate Broker		C
Real Estate Salesperson		C
Retail Management	A	C
Advance		C
Foundation		C
Intermediate		C
Small Business Accounting	A	
Bookkeeping for a Small Business		C
Income Tax Preparation Internship		C
Recordkeeping for a Small Business		C
Small Business Management Community Service		
Business Presentation		C
Enactus		C
Working Education		C
Small Business Management Entrepreneur	A	C
Business Comm. & Cultural Competence		C
Business Presentations		C
Management and Team Building		C
Starting and Managing a Small Business		C
Writing and Computational Skills for Business		C
Child Development	A	
Assistant Teacher		C
Family Child Care		C
Infant/Toddler Care		C
Residential Care Worker		C
School Age Child Care		C
Site Supervisor	A	
Child Development Teacher (Permit Preparation)		
Associate Teacher		C
Master Teacher		C
Teacher		C
Computer Business Technology		
Administrative Office Management	A	C
Basics: Computer, Office Support, Records Management		C
Records Information Management	A	C
Computer Information Systems	A	C
Desktop Support Technician		C
Information Technology Management	A	C
Computer Technical Illustration (CTI)	A	C
Construction Trades		
Electrical	A	C
Sheet Metal	A	C
Cosmetology	A	C
Esthetician		C
Electricity		
Electrical Controls Systems		C
Electricity	A	C
Electricity, Lineman	A	C
Electronics		C
Electronic Communication Systems	A	C
Electronic Microprocessor/Microcontroller Design	A	C
Electronics Technician Level 1		C
Fitness Specialist		C
Graphic Design	A	C
Human Services		
Community Health Work		C
Mental Health Work		C
Youth Development Work		C
Machine Technology		
Computer Aided Manufacturing	A	C
Computerized Numerical Control Operator		C
Computerized Numerical Control Technology		C
Manufacturing Engineering Technology		
Advanced Manufacturing		C
Electromechanical Engineering Technology		C
Electronics Manufacturing		C
Fabrication Manufacturing		C

A—Associate Degree Program C—Certificate Program

SAN DIEGO CITY COLLEGE continued

Introduction to Manufacturing		C
Manufacturing Fundamentals		C
Music: Digital Music Technology	A	
Digital Audio		C
Recording Arts		C
Nursing Education		
LVN to RN	A	
Registered Nurse	A	
Photography	A	C
Radio, Television and Film		
Broadcast News	A	C
Management	A	
Multimedia	A	
Performance		C
Radio	A	C
Video/Film	A	C
Shipbuilding Technology	A	C

WE'RE SORRY THAT WE COULDN'T GET AN APPROVAL OF THE ACCURACY OF THESE PROGRAMS BUT THIS IS THE RESPONSE WE GOT:

"Mr. Meyer, You have no authority or permission to post or print anything related to San Diego City College. Please cease and desist contacting anyone at the college, and do not post nor print anything related to City College.

Dr. Anthony E. Beebe, President"

A—Associate Degree Program C—Certificate Program

SAN DIEGO MESA COLLEGE

7250 Mesa College Dr
San Diego CA 92111-4998
619-388-2600
619-388-2929 Fax
www.sdmesa.edu

Dr. Tim McGrath, Vice President of Instruction

Enrollment: Full-time 6,531 Part-time 16,212

Semester system; One 8 week summer session (day)
One 8 week summer session (eve)
Two 5 week summer sessions (day)

No Housing

OCCUPATIONAL PROGRAMS

Accounting	A	C
American Sign Language	A	C
Animal Health Technology	A	
Architecture	A	C
Architecture Technician	A	C
Computer Aided Drafting		C
Construction Management	A	C
Landscape Architecture	A	C
Landscape Architecture Technician	A	C
Building Construction Technology	A	C
Business		
Administration	A	C
Management	A	C
Child Development	A	
Assistant Teacher		C
Associate Teacher		C
Home Day Care		C
Master Teacher		C
Teacher		C
Computer and Information Science	A	C
Computer Programing		C
Computer Business Technology		
Administrative Assistant	A	C
Desktop Publishing		C
General Office Clerk		C
Information Management Technology	A	C
Keyboarder/Word Processor		C
Microcomputer Applications	A	C
Culinary Arts/Management in Hospitality	A	C
Dental Assisting	A	C
Engineering	A	C
Fashion	A	C
Computer Fashion Technology: Design	A	C
Computer Fashion Technology: Merchandising	A	C
Design	A	C
Merchandising	A	C
Geographic Information Systems	A	
Technician		C
Health Information Technology	A	
Hospitality	A	C
Event Management	A	C
Hotel Management	A	C
Interior Design	A	C
Journalism	A	C
Marketing	A	C
Medical Assisting	A	C
Multimedia		
3D Animation and Modeling		C
Digital Video		C
Flash		C
Interactive Media Production		C
Multimedia	A	
Multimedia Survey		C
New Media Publishing		C
Video Game Development		C
Nutrition	A	C
Dietetic Service Supervisor		C
Nutrition and Fitness	A	C
Physical Education	A	
Fitness Specialist		C
Physical Therapist Assistant	A	
Radiologic Technology	A	C
Real Estate	A	

A—Associate Degree Program C—Certificate Program

SAN DIEGO MIRAMAR COLLEGE

10440 Black Mountain Rd
San Diego CA 92126-2999
619-388-7800
619-388-7911 Fax
www.sdmiramar.edu

Lynne Ornelas, Business, Technical Careers and Workforce Initiatives

Enrollment: Full-time 3,500 Part-time 6,500

Semester system; Two 5 week summer sessions

No Housing

OCCUPATIONAL PROGRAMS

Administration of Justice	A	C
Automotive Technology	A	C
Aviation Maintenance Technology	A	C
Aviation Operations	A	C
Business Administration	A	C
Business Management	A	C
Child Development	A	C
Communication Studies	A	
Computer and Information Science	A	C
Computer Business Technology	A	C
Diesel Technology	A	C
Emergency Medical Care		C
Fire Protection Technology	A	C
Medical Laboratory Technician Training	A	C
Paralegal	A	C

A—Associate Degree Program C—Certificate Program

CITY COLLEGE OF SAN FRANCISCO

1400 Evans Ave
San Francisco CA 94124
415-550-4440
415-550-4400 Fax
www.ccsf.edu

Tom Boegel, Associate Vice Chancellor of Workforce and Economic Development

Enrollment: Full-time & Part-time 110,000

Semester system; 6 and 7 week summer session

No Housing

OCCUPATIONAL PROGRAMS

Administration of Justice	A	C
Forensic Identification		C
Aircraft Maintenance Technology	A	C
Aircraft Powerplant Maintenance Technology	A	C
Airframe-Maintenance Technology		C
Architecture	A	
Construction Management	A	C
Interior Design Major	A	
Auto Body Technology		
Damage Analysis and Estimating		C
Painting and Refinishing		C
Structural Analysis and Damage Repair		C
Non-Structural Analysis Damage Repair		C
Automotive Technology		
Alternative Fuel Technology		C
Brake and Suspension Specialist	A	C
Engine Performance and Drivability		C
Engine Repair Specialist		C
General Automotive Technician		C
Mechanics	A	
Transmission Specialist		C
Avionics-Maintenance Technology	A	C
Broadcast Electronic Media Arts		
Audio and Video for the Web		C
Broadcast Motion Graphics		C
Convergent Media Production		C
Digital Radio Management		C
Digital Radio News and Public Affairs		C
Digital Radio Performance and Production		C
Live Sound		C
Multimedia Journalism		C
Sound Design		C
Sound Recording		C
Television Production		C
Video Post-Production		C
Video Production and Editing		C
Business		
Accounting	A	
Accounting—Microcomputer		C
Administrative Support	A	
Finance	A	C
General Business	A	C
Green and Sustainable Business		C
Green and Sustainable Travel		C
Marketing	A	C
Paralegal/Legal Studies	A	C
Real Estate	A	C
Retail Management		C
Supervision and Management		C
Travel and Tourism Major	A	C
Travel and Tourism Management		C
Travel and Tourism Destination Specialist		C
Child Development and Family Studies		
Administration		C
Appreciating Diversity		C
Child Development	A	
Family Child Care		C
Infant/Toddler Care		C
Practitioner		C
Pre-Teacher		C
Professional Development and Advocacy		C
School-Age Care		C
Violence Intervention in Early Childhood		C
Youth Worker		C
Cinema Production	A	
Computer Networking & Information Technology	A	
Advanced Cybersecurity		C
Computer Technical Support		C
Computer Technician		C
Cybersecurity		C
Fundamentals of Networking		C
Fundamentals of Technical Support		C
Mobile Web Development		C
Network Security		C
Routing and Switching (Cisco)		C
Website Development Techniques		C
Windows Networking		C
Wireless Networking		C
Computer Science	A	
Android App Programming		C
Computer Programming C++		C
Computer Programming JAVA		C
Computer Programming Visual Basic with Databases		C

A—Associate Degree Program C—Certificate Program

CITY COLLEGE OF SAN FRANCISCO (continued)

Computing Skills for Scientists		C
Database Programming: MySQL/Open Source Technologies		C
Database Programming: Oracle		C
iPhone App Programming		C
Linux Administration I		C
QA, Build and Release Automation		C
Web Application Programming		C
Construction		
Carpentry		C
Residential Plumbing		C
Residential Wiring		C
Solar Hot Water Systems		C
Culinary Arts and Hospitality Studies	A	
Culinary Arts Management	A	
Food Service Management	A	
Hotel Management	A	
Dental Assisting	A	C
Engineering and Technology		
Basic Electronics		C
Biomanufacturing		C
Biomedical Equipment Technician (BMET)		C
Bioprocess Instrumentation and Control		C
Biotechnology	A	C
Biotechnology Lab Assistant		C
Computer Aided Design (CAD)		C
Computer Aided Drafting (CAD)		C
Electronic Engineering Technology	A	
Engineering—General	A	
Engineered Plumbing Systems		C
Environmental Control Technology		C
Genomics Technology		C
Geographic Information Systems (GIS)		C
Heating, Ventilation, Air Conditioning and Refrigeration		C
Intermediate Electronics		C
Manufacturing and Fabrication		C
Sustainability		C
Stem Cell Technology		C
Welding—Combination		C
Environmental Horticulture and Floristry		
Commercial Cut-Flower and Greenhouse Production	A	C
Floristry	A	
Landscape Construction		C
Landscape Design		C
Landscape Gardening and Landscape Contracting	A	C
Landscape Maintenance		C
Nursery and Garden Center Operation	A	C
Fashion		
Fashion Design	A	C
Fashion Merchandising	A	C
Fashion Styling		C
Image Consultant		C
Textiles		C
Health Care Technology		
CVT/Echocardiography	A	C
EKG Technician		C
Emergency Medical Technician		C
Health Information Clerk I, II		C
Health Information Coding Specialist		C
Health Information Technology	A	C
Medical Administrative Assisting	A	
Medical Biller		C
Medical Evaluation Assistant		C
Medical Office Assisting	A	C
Medical Receptionist		C
Paramedic	A	C
Pharmacy Technician		C
Health Education	A	
Community Health Worker		C
Community Mental Health		C
Drug and Alcohol Studies		C
Health Care Interpreter		C
Infectious Disease Prevention in Priority Populations		C
Nutrition Assistant		C
Post-Prison Health Worker Specialty		C
Youth Worker: Organizing, Advocacy, Counseling and Education		C
Journalism	A	
Editorial Management and Design		C
On-line Research		C
Labor and Community Studies	A	C
Cesar Chavez Advocacy		C
Solidarity Forever/Si Se Puede Advocacy		C
Library Information Technology	A	C
Motorcycle Technology		
Engine and Power Train Repair		C
General Service		C
Technician	A	
Tune-up, Electrical, and Performance		C
Nursing		
Home Health Aide/Nurse Assistant		C
Registered	A	
Vocational		C
Photography	A	
Architectural		C
Collaborative Design		C
Digital		C
Portrait Lighting		C
Studio Lighting		C
Radiologic Sciences		
Diagnostic Medical Imaging	A	
Radiation Therapy Technology	A	

A—Associate Degree Program C—Certificate Program

CITY COLLEGE OF SAN FRANCISCO (continued)

Visual Media Design		
Collaborative Design		C
Digital Animation		C
Digital Art Foundation		C
Digital Illustration		C
Digital Printing and Document Management		C
Game Development		C
Graphic Design	A	C
Visual Design Foundation		C
Visual Media Production		C
Web Foundation		C
Web Front-end Development		C

SAN JOAQUIN DELTA COLLEGE

5151 Pacific Ave
Stockton CA 95207-6370
209-954-5151
209-954-5600 Fax
www.deltacollege.edu

Salvador Vargas, Dean of CTE and Workforce Development

Enrollment: Full-time 9,000 Part-time 10,000

Semester system; 6 week summer session

No Housing

OCCUPATIONAL PROGRAMS

Agriculture and Natural Resources		
Agriculture Business	A	C
Agriculture Engineering	A	
Agriculture Mechanics		C
Horticulture	A	
Horticulture–Landscape Management		C
Horticulture–Nursery Management		C
Horticulture–Turf Grass		C
American Sign Language		C
Arts, Media and Entertainment Technology		
Graphic Arts		C
Media Studies w/Concentration in Radio	A	C
Media Studies w/Concentration in Television	A	C
Photography	A	
Theater Arts–Acting	A	
Theatre Arts–Technical Theatre	A	
Building Trades and Construction		
Caterpillar Dealer Service Technician	A	
Electrical Technology		C
Electronics Technology		C
Electron Microscopy: Biological or Crystalline		C
Heating and Air Conditioning-Refrigeration	A	C
Heavy Equipment Mechanic		C
Heavy Equipment Technician	A	C
Refrigeration		C
Welding Technology		C
Early Childhood Education	A	
Associate Teacher		C
Master Teacher		C
Site Supervisor		C
Teacher		C
Education Aide		C
Education, Child Development and Family Service		
Communication: Speech Language Pathology Assistant (SLPA)	A	C
Communications Studies	A	
Family and Consumer Sciences	A	
Eligibility Worker		C
Energy and Utilities		
Automotive Body Repair		C
Automotive Dealer Technician		C
Automotive Electric Technology		C
Automotive Master Technician		C
Automotive Mechanics Technology		C
Diesel Automotive Equipment Technician		C
Diesel Equipment Technician	A	C
Fluid Power and Automation Technology	A	C
Engineering and Design		
Architectural Drafting	A	C
Civil Technology	A	
Engineering	A	C
Engineering Computer-Aided Drafter		C
Engineering Technologies	A	
Engineering Technology (Civil, Electro-Mechanical or Mechanical)	A	C
Fashion and Interior Design		
Apparel Design	A	C
Fashion Merchandising	A	C
Interior Design	A	C
Finance and Business		
Accounting	A	C
Administrative Assistant		C
Basic Business		C
Bookkeeping		C
Business–General	A	
General Office		C
International Business		C
Municipal Clerk		C
Office Assistant		C
Office Management	A	C
Real Estate		C
Supervision and Management		C
Tax Preparation		C
Health Science and Medical Technology		
Family and Consumer Sciences	A	
Fitness Specialist		C
Nursing RN	A	C
Psychiatric Technician		C
Radiologic Technology	A	C
Hospitality, Tourism and Recreation		
Baking and Pastry	A	C
Culinary Arts	A	
Culinary Arts, Advanced	A	C

A—Associate Degree Program C—Certificate Program

SAN JOAQUIN DELTA COLLEGE

Human Services Worker–Gerontology Specialist		C
Human Services Worker–Family Abuse Specialist		C
Information Technology		
Computer Information System	A	
Computer Networking–Competence		C
Computer Networking–Essentials		C
Computer Networking–Software	A	C
Computer Networking–Technician		C
Computer Operations		C
Computer Programming–Competence		C
Computer Programming–Essentials		C
Computer Science	A	C
Computer Support		C
Computer Support–Technician		C
Computer Web Developer		C
Computer Web Developer–Technician		C
Manufacturing and Product Development		
Industrial Technology		C
Machine Shop Technology		C
Marketing, Sales and Service		
Merchandising	A	C
Retail Management	A	C
Mental Health Specialist		C
Public Services		
Basic Peace Officer Academy		C
Correctional Science	A	C
Fire Science	A	C
Law Enforcement	A	C
Recreation Assistant		C
Substance Abuse Counselor		C
Transportation	A	
Logistics and Transportation Supervisor		C
Traffic Shipping and Receiving Technician		C

SAN JOSE CITY COLLEGE

2100 Moorpark Ave
San Jose CA 95128-2799
408-298-2181
408-293-0625 Fax
www.sjcc.edu

Ingrid Thompson, Business and Workforce Development Division

Enrollment: Full-time 4,932 Part-time 20,854

16 week semester system; 6 week summer session

No Housing

OCCUPATIONAL PROGRAMS

Accounting	A	C
Administration of Justice	A	
Judicial Administration	A	C
Traditional Option	A	
Air Conditioning	A	C
Alcohol and Drug Program Technician	A	C
Business		
Entrepreneurship	A	C
Management	A	C
Marketing	A	C
Computer Applications	A	C
Computer Information System		
CCNA		C
CCNP	A	C
General Networks	A	C
Network Administration A+		C
Novell		C
MCSA		C
MCSE	A	C
Programming	A	C
Unix	A	C
Web Developer	A	C
Construction Technology	A	C
Residential Building Maintenance		C
Residential Carpentry		C
Cosmetology/Manicuring/Esthetician	A	C
Dental Assisting	A	C
Early Childhood Education	A	C
Emergency Medical Technician		C
Facilities Maintenance	A	C
Labor Studies	A	C
Laser Technology	A	C
Machine Technology (including CNC)	A	C
Media Arts	A	C
Print Media		C
Motion Arts		C
Web/Interactive Design		C
Medical Assisting: Administrative	A	C
Clinical	A	C
Real Estate	A	C

A—Associate Degree Program C—Certificate Program

COLLEGE OF SAN MATEO

1700 W Hillsdale Blvd
San Mateo CA 94402-3784
650-574-6161
650-574-6680 Fax
www.collegeofsanmateo.edu

Sandra Stefani,Vice President of Instruction
Kathleen Ross, Primary OCC ED Dean

Enrollment: Full-time 3,026 Part-time 7,873

Semester system; Concurrent 6 and 8 week summer sessions

No Housing

OCCUPATIONAL PROGRAMS

Accounting	A	C
Assistant	A	C
CPA Exam Preparation: Business Environment and Regulations		C
CPA Exam Preparation: Financial Accounting and Auditing		C
Enrolled Agent Exam Preparation		C
Tax Preparer I, II		C
Addiction Studies	A	C
Co-occurring Disorders		C
Administration of Justice	A	C
Architecture	A	
Art		
Photography	A	
Building Inspection Technology	A	C
Business		
Business Administration	A	
Business Administration, Option 1	A	
Business Administration, Option 2	A	
Microcomputer/Database and Spreadsheet	A	C
Microcomputer/Office Assistant	A	C
Office Assistant I, II		C
Computer and Information Science (CIS)	A	
C++ Programming		C
Computer Science Applications and Development	A	C
Internet Programming		C
Java Programming		C
Web and Mobile Application Development	A	C
Web/Mobile App Development		C
Cosmetology	A	C
Dental Assisting	A	C
Digital Media		
Digital Video		C
Digital Video Production		C
Graphic Production		C
Web Design/Multimedia	A	C
Drafting/CAD	A	C
Computer Aided Design		C
Electrical Technology		
Inside Wireman		C
Electronics Technology		C

Advanced Electrical Power Systems and Instrumentation		C
Electrical Power Systems and Instrumentation		C
Fundamentals of Smart Building Systems		C
Telecommunications Fundamentals		C
Engineering		
Engineering Technology-General	A	
Fire Technology	A	C
Kinesiology	A	
Comprehensive Pilates Instructor		C
Group Fitness Instructor		C
Personal Trainer		C
Pilates Mat and Reformer Instructor		C
Pilates Mat Instructor		C
Specialized Pilates Instructor		C
Yoga Instructor		C
Management		
Business Management	A	C
Human Resources Management		C
Marketing Management	A	C
Project Management		C
Retail Management	A	C
Music	A	
Electronic Music	A	C
Nursing	A	
Real Estate	A	

A—Associate Degree Program C—Certificate Program

SANTA ANA COLLEGE

1530 W 17th St
Santa Ana CA 92706
714-564-6000
714-564-6455 Fax
www.sac.edu

Omar Torres, Vice President

Enrollment: Full-time 4,215 Part-time 23,743

Semester system 16 weeks; 6 or 8 week summer session; 4 week intersession in January

No Housing

OCCUPATIONAL PROGRAMS

Accounting	A	
Accounting and Financial Planning		C
Accounting with Sage MAS Software		C
Computerized Accounting–QuickBooks		C
Computerized Bookkeeping–QuickBooks		C
Computerized Bookkeeping–Sage MAS Software		C
Enrolled Agent		C
General		C
Microsoft Dynamics for Financial Accounting		C
American Sign Language		C
Art		
3-D Animation–Television/Video Communications		C
3-D Modeling and Animation–Art Emphasis		C
3-D Modeling and Animation–Video Game and Interactive Media Art Emphasis		C
3-D Modeling and Animation–Previsualization		C
Art-Graphic Design	A	
Digital Media Arts	A	
Digital Media Arts–Graphic Design		C
Digital Media Arts–Web Design		C
Automotive Technology	A	C
Advance Engine Performance		C
Chassis Service		C
Drive Train Service		C
Engine Performance and Electrical		C
Engine Service		C
Biotechnology Lab Assistant		C
Business Administration	A	
Business Applications & Technology	A	C
Bilingual		C
Digital Publishing	A	C
Microsoft Office Professional	A	C
Office Management	A	C
Communications and Media Studies	A	C
Computer Information Systems	A	C
Database		C
Enterprise Systems		C
Help Desk		C
Networking		C
PC Maintenance and Troubleshooting		C
UNIX		C
Web Programming		C
Computer Science	A	C
Programming		C
Criminal Justice	A	
Corrections Officer		C
Law Enforcement		C
Diesel Technology		
Diesel and Heavy Equipment Technology	A	C
Mid-Range Engine Service	A	C
Transport Refrigeration/Temperature Control		C
Engineering	A	
Civil Technology	A	C
Computer-Aided Drafting & Design	A	C
Drafting and Design–Option I, II	A	C
Energy Analysis	A	C
Industrial Technology	A	C
Mechanical 3D Solid Modeling CAD		C
Sustainable Facilities Management		C
Entrepreneurship and Innovation	A	C
Freelancer		C
Fashion Design	A	C
Product Development and Technical Design	A	C
Dressmaking and Alteration		C
Merchandising	A	C
Fire Technology		
Administrative Fire Services Chief Officer	A	C
Administration	A	C
Prevention Officer	A	C
Public Fire Service	A	C
Human Development		
Early Childhood	A	C
Bilingual Preschool Associate Teacher		C
Infant Toddler	A	C
Preschool Child	A	C
School Age	A	C
International Business	A	C
Global Trade Skills		C
Library Technology	A	C

A—Associate Degree Program C—Certificate Program

SANTA ANA COLLEGE (continued)

Management	A	C
Human Resources Management		C
Retail Management	A	C
Small Business	A	C
Supervision		C
Manufacturing Technology		
CNC Lathe Set Up and Operation	A	C
CNC Machine Set Up and Operation	A	C
CNC Milling Machine Set Up and Operation	A	C
CNC Programmer A-Mastercam	A	C
Conventional Machining	A	C
Solidworks 3D Solid Modeling		C
Marketing	A	C
Medical Assistant - Administrative/Clinical	A	C
Music		
Digital Music Production		C
Nursing - Registered Nursing	A	
Nutrition and Dietetics	A	
Culinary Arts		C
Hospitality		C
Occupational Therapy Assistant	A	
Paralegal	A	C
Pharmacy Technology	A	C
Photography	A	
Commercial		C
Speech/Language Pathology Assistant	A	
TV/Video Communications	A	
Broadcast Journalism		C
Computer Graphics and Animation for Video		C
Media Studies		C
Television Production		C
Television Scriptwriter		C
Theatre Arts		
Entertainment Lighting Technology		C
Performance	A	
Technical	A	
Welding Technology	A	C

A—Associate Degree Program   C—Certificate Programs

SANTA BARBARA CITY COLLEGE

721 Cliff Drive
Santa Barbara CA 93109-2394
805-965-0581
805-963-7222 Fax
www.sbcc.edu

Alan Price, Ph.D., Dean, Educational Programs

Enrollment: Full-time 7,965 Part-time 12,024

Semester system; 6 week summer session

No Housing

OCCUPATIONAL PROGRAMS

Accounting		
Accounting	A	
Accounting/Assistant Bookkeeper, Level IV		C
Bookkeeping	SCA	
Alcohol and Drug Counseling		
Alcohol and Drug Counseling	A	C
Post-Professional Practice in ADC		C
Allied Health		
Emergency Medical Technician	SCA	
Business Administration		
Business Administration (SCA)	A	C
Entrepreneurship	A	C
Management	A	C
Real Estate	A	C
Computer Applications & Office Management		
Business Communications	SCA	
Business Software Specialist	A	C
Computer Applications & Office Management	A	C
Computer Proficiency Online	SCA	
Office Assistant	SCA	
Office Management	A	C
Computer Information Systems		
Accounting Information Systems	SCA	
Computer Information Systems	A	C
Database Programing and Applications Development		C
Help Desk and Desktop Support	SCA	
Information Technology Management	SCA	
Microsoft Office Development	SCA	
Microsoft SQL Server Database Administration	SCA	
Microsoft Windows System Administration and Security	SCA	
Mobile Device Administration	SCA	
PC Support/Network Management		C
Technical Writing	SCA	
Virtualization System Administration	SCA	
Web Server Administration	SCA	
Computer Network Engineering		
Cisco Networking Associate	SCA	
Computer Network Engineering	A	C

Construction Technology	A	C
Cosmetology		
Cosmetology	A	C
Esthetician	SCA	
Manicure	SCA	
Culinary Arts & Hotel Management		
Baking & Pastry	SCA	
Culinary Arts	A	C
Hospitality	A	C
Hospitality Operations Specialist	SCA	
Human Resource Hospitality Specialist	SCA	
Personal Chef Training	SCA	
Drafting/CAD	A	C
Early Childhood Education		
Associate Child Care Teacher		C
Diversity Issues in ECE		C
Early Childhood Education	A	C
Infant Toddler Development		C
School-Age Care		C
Environmental Horticulture		
Ecological Restoration and Management	A	
Environmental Horticulture	A	C
Landscape Contracting C-27 License	A	
Landscape Design	A	
Landscape Operations	SCA	
Nursery/Greenhouse Technology	A	
Sustainable Horticulture	SCA	
Film and Television		
Film and Television Production	A	
Film Studies	A	
Finance, International Business, and Marketing		
Finance	A	C
International Business	A	C
International Marketing Communication	SCA	
Marketing	A	C
Sales and Marketing	SCA	
Web Marketing and Media Design	SCA	
Graphic Design and Photography		
Graphic Design	A	C
Graphic Design and Photography	A	C

A—Associate Degree Program C—Certificate Program SCA—Skills Competency Award

SANTA BARBARA CITY COLLEGE

Health Information Technology and Cancer Information Management	
Cancer Information Management	A C
Health Information Technology	A
Medical Coding Specialist	C
Interior Design	A C
Journalism	
Broadcast Journalism	A C
Journalism	A C
Photojournalism	SCA
Public Relations	SCA
Visual Journalism	A C
Marine Diving Technologies	
Commercial Diving	SCA
Marine Diving Technician	A C
Multimedia Arts and Technologies	
Animation and Gaming	A C
Media Arts	A C
Media Design and Development	SCA
Mobile Media Core	SCA
Web Marketing and Media Design	SCA
Physical Education/Health Education/ Dance/Athletics	
Physical Education	A
Radiographic and Imaging Sciences; Diagnostic Medical Sonography	
Diagnostic Medical Sonography	C
Radiography	A
School of Justice Studies	
Administration of Justice	A C
Criminology	A C
Law Enforcement	A C
Legal Studies	A C
School of Nursing	
Acute Care	SCA
Certified Nursing Assistant	SCA
Home Health Aide	SCA
Nursing, LVN	A C
Nursing, RN/ADN	A
Water Science	
Wastewater Collection	C
Wastewater Treatment	C
Water Distribution	C
Water Treatment	C

A—Associate Degree Program C—Certificate Program SCA—Skills Competency Award

SANTA MONICA COLLEGE

1900 Pico Blvd
Santa Monica CA 90405-1628
310-434-4000
www.smc.edu

Dr. Patricia G. Ramos, Dean-Workforce and Economic Development

Enrollment: Full and Part-time 33,700

Semester system, 6 week summer session, 6 week winter session

No Housing

OCCUPATIONAL PROGRAMS

Program	A	C
Accounting	A	C
Computer Accounting		C
Professional Accountant		C
Automotive Technology		C
Business Administration		
Entrepreneurship		C
Insurance Professional	A	C
Insurance Specialist		C
International Business		C
Logistics/Supply Chain Management	A	C
Management/Leadership	A	C
Marketing		C
Merchandising	A	C
Professional	A	
Communication and Media Studies		
Broadcast Programming and Production	A	C
Broadcast Sales and Management	A	C
Communications	A	
Entertainment Promotions and Marketing "Promo Pathway"	A	C
Film Production	A	C
Film Studies	A	
Journalism	A	
Computer Science Information Systems		
Computer Business Applications	A	C
Digital Publishing		C
Website Creator		C
Website Development Management		C
Website Software Specialist	A	C
Computer Science	A	C
Computer Programming	A	C
Database Applications Developer	A	C
Information Systems Management		C
Mobile Application Development-Android		C
Mobile Application Development-iPhone		C
Networking		C
Web Programmer	A	C
Cosmetology	A	C
Nail Care		C
Salon Business		C
Skin Care		C
Teacher Training		C
Early Childhood Education	A	C
Early Childhood Education Core		C
Intervention Assistant	A	C
School-Age Intervention Assistant		C
Entertainment Technology		
2D Animation		C
3D Animation		C
3D Modeling		C
3D Rendering		C
Animation	A	C
Digital Effects		C
Digital Media	A	C
Game Design		C
Fashion Design and Merchandising		
Design	A	C
Merchandising	A	C
Graphic Design	A	C
Web Design		C
Health Sciences		
Nursing-RN	A	
Respiratory Therapy	A	
Interior Architectural Design	A	C
CAD Production and Design		C
Set Design and Art Direction for Film and TV		C
Office Technology		
Clerical/Data Entry		C
General Office	A	C
Legal Administrative Assistant	A	C
Medical Administrative Assistant	A	C
Medical Billing/Coding		C
Medical Coding and Billing Specialist	A	C
Medical Records Clerk Receptionist		C
Medical Transcription		C
Word Processing		C
Photography	A	C
Sustainable Technologies		
Energy Efficiency Specialist		C
Recycling and Resource Management	A	C
Solar Photovoltaic Installation	A	C
Theatre Arts	A	C
Technical Theatre	A	C

A—Associate Degree Program C—Certificate Program

SANTA ROSA JUNIOR COLLEGE

1501 Mendocino Ave
Santa Rosa CA 95401-4395
707-527-4011
707-527-4816 Fax
www.santarosa.edu

Jerry Miller, Dean III, Career and Technical Education & Economic Development

Enrollment: Full-time 7,251 Part-time 18,727

Semester system; 6 and 8 week summer sessions plus several short courses

No Housing

OCCUPATIONAL PROGRAMS

Accounting/Bookkeeping		
Accountant Assistant		C
Account Clerk		C
Bookkeeper		C
Bookkeeper Assistant		C
Payroll		C
Tax Assistant Clerk		C
Administration of Justice for Transfer	A	
Children in the Justice System		C
Corrections		C
Administrative		
Administrative Assistant		C
Administrative Office Professional	A	
Legal Office Support		C
Legal Secretary		C
Office Assistant		C
Paralegal Studies	A	
Adobe Applications		
Adobe Applications Specialist		C
Illustrator		C
InDesign		C
Photoshop		C
Agribusiness		
Agriculture Business Management	A	C
Animal Science	A	
Architecture Major	A	
Automotive Technology	A	C
Brakes, Steering and Suspension Specialist		C
Electric and Electronic Systems Specialist		C
Engine Repair Specialist		C
Heating, Ventilating and Air Conditioning Systems Specialist		C
Transmission Specialist		C
Tune-Up and Electronic Specialist		C
Business Marketing		C
Child Development	A	
Associate Teacher (Preschool)		C
Teacher (Preschool)		C
Civil Engineering Technology	A	C
Community Health Worker	A	C
Corrections		
Corrections Officer Basic Course		C
Juvenile Correctional Office Basic Course		C
Probation Officer Basic Course		C
Counseling		
Advocacy	A	C
Alcohol and Drug	A	C
Culinary Arts	A	C
Baking & Pastry		C
Dining Room Service		C
Front House Operations		C
Restaurant Management	A	C
Dental Assisting		C
Dental Hygiene	A	
Diesel Technology		
Chassis		C
Diesel Equipment Technology	A	C
Electrical/Electronics		C
Equipment Technology		C
Heating, Ventilation and Cooling		C
Power Train		C
Preventive Maintenance (T8)		C
Digital Media		
3D Modeling and Animation	A	C
Audio	A	C
Digital Filmmaking	A	C
Game Programming	A	
Interactive Multimedia	A	C
Electronic Technology		
Automated Test and Controls		C
Electro-Mechanical Maintenance Tech		C
Electronics Technology	A	C
Solar Photovoltaic		C
Emergency Medical Technician (EMT)		
Advance Cardiac Life Support		C
Basic Arrhythmia Recognition Source		C
Emergency Care for First Responders		C
EMT-1 Refresher		C
EMT–Basic		C
Paramedic	A	C

A—Associate Degree Program C—Certificate Program

SANTA ROSA JUNIOR COLLEGE (continued)

Entrepreneurship		C
Environmental Conservation		
Natural Resource Management	A	C
Parks and Recreation Management	A	C
Watershed Management	A	C
Environmental Horticulture		
Basic Horticulture		C
Garden Design	A	C
Landscape Management	A	C
Nursery Management	A	C
Equine Science	A	C
Fashion Studies		
Fashion Design Assistant	A	C
Retail Merchandising	A	C
Firefighter 1 Academy		C
Fire Technology	A	C
Fitness, Nutrition and Health	A	C
Flower Design	A	C
Geospatial Technology	A	C
Graphic Design	A	C
Graphic Design Production Fundamentals		C
Hospitality		
Front Office Management		C
Wine Tasting Service		C
Information Technology/Networking		
Cisco Certification Training in CCNA		C
Computer Science	A	C
IT Support		C
Microsoft Office Specialist		C
Interior Design		
Commercial	A	C
Residential	A	C
Retail Merchandising	A	C
Journalism and Journalism for Transfer	A	
Law Enforcement		
Advance Officer Training		C
Background Investigation		C
Basic Police Officer Academy		C
Law Enforcement		C
Law Enforcement Supervisor Techniques		C
Public Safety Dispatcher Basic Course		C
Machine Tool Technology	A	C
Basic CNC Lathe		C
Basic CNC Mill		C
Basic Manual Machine Tool Technology		C
Management		
Business Management		C
Human Resource Administration		C
Retail Management		C
Medical Assisting		
Administrative	A	C
Administrative and Clinical	A	C
Clinical	A	C
Nursing		
ADN	A	
Certified Nurse Assistant		C
Home Health Aide		C
Vocational Nursing	A	C
Vocational Nursing to Nursing (ADN)	A	
Nutrition and Dietetic Technology	A	C
Dietary Service Supervisor		C
Dietetic Technician	A	
Nutrition and Dietetics	A	
Pharmacy Technician	A	C
Phlebotomy		C
Radiologic Technology	A	C
Ranger Academy		C
Real Estate		C
Real Estate Sales		C
Surveying Technology	A	C
Sustainable Agriculture	A	C
Veterinary Technician		C
Viticulture	A	C
Water Resources Technology		
Water Utility Operations		C
Wastewater Treatment Technology		C
Web		
Designer		C
Fundamentals		
Programmer		C
Project Management		C
Welding Technology		C
Wine Studies		
Enology	A	C
Wine Business and Marketing	A	C
Wine Evaluation and Service	A	C

A—Associate Degree Program C—Certificate Program

SANTIAGO CANYON COLLEGE

8045 E Chapman Avenue
Orange CA 92869-4512
714-628-4900
www.sccollege.edu

Carol Comeau, Interim Dean of Business & Career Technical Education

Enrollment: Full-time 2,312 Part-time 5,727

Semester system 16 weeks; 4 or 8 week summer session

No Housing

OCCUPATIONAL PROGRAMS

Accounting	A	C
Art-Graphic Design	A	C
Biology		
Biotechnology	A	
Biotechnology Biomanufacturing Technician		C
Biotechnology Lab Assistant		C
Biotechnology Laboratory Technician: Food Safety		C
General Biotechnology Technician		C
Business Administration	A	
Business Management	A	
Entrepreneurship	A	C
Computer Information Systems	A	C
Computer Science	A	C
Applied Robotics & Embedded Programing		C
Cosmetology	A	C
Esthetician		C
Manicuring		C
Electrician-General	A	C
Gemology	A	C
Human Development		
Infant/Toddler		C
Preschool		C
School Age Child		C
Management		
General Management	A	
Human Resources Management		C
Supervision		C
Marketing		
Advertising		C
General Marketing	A	C
Web Marketing		C
Public Works		
Code Enforcement Officer		C
Construction Inspection	A	C
Construction Management	A	C
Environmental Management	A	C
Real Estate	A	C
Real Estate Appraisal		C
Real Estate Salesperson		C
Surveying		
Land Surveying	A	C
Television/Video Communications: Media Studies		C
Water Utility Science		
Distribution	A	C
Treatment	A	C
Wastewater/Environmental Sanitation	A	C

A—Associate Degree Program C—Certificate Program

COLLEGE OF THE SEQUOIAS

4999 E Bardsley Ave.
Tulare CA 93277
559-688-3027
559-687-6294 Fax
www.cos.edu

Dr. C Louann Waldner, Dean, Career Technical Education and Workforce Development

Enrollment: Full-time 9,000 (Full-time equivalent students)

Semester system; 6 week summer session

No Housing

OCCUPATIONAL PROGRAMS

Program		
Administration of Justice		
Basic Police Academy (P.O.S.T. Certified)		C
Corrections	A	C
Law Enforcement	A	C
Agriculture		C
Agricultural Business Management	A	C
Agricultural Pest Management		C
Agricultural Power Equipment Technician		C
Agricultural Power Equipment Technology		C
Agricultural Science		C
Agricultural Technology		C
Agricultural Transportation		C
Agriculture and Environmental Science	A	C
Animal Science	A	C
Dairy Science	A	C
Equine Science		C
Architecture	A	C
Autodesk AutoCAD for Architecture		C
Autodesk AutoCAD for Drafting		C
Autodesk Maya		C
Design		C
Drafting		C
History		C
Visual Communication		C
Automotive Technology, Basic	A	C
Air Conditioning Technology		C
Brake Systems		C
Chassis Technology		C
Electrical Technology		C
Emissions Technology		C
Engine Technology		C
Power Train System Technology		C
Business		
Accounting	A	C
Administrative Assistant	A	C
Business General	A	C
Business Financial Recordkeeping		C
Computer and Information System	A	C
Computer Applications		C
Computerized Office Procedures	A	C
Interpreter Certificate (Spanish)		C
Law Office Clerk/Receptionist		C
Legal Secretary		C
Marketing Management		C
Paralegal	A	C
Word Processing		C
Child Development	A	C
Assistant		C
Associate Teacher		C
Special Education		C
Cisco CCNA Academy		C
Commercial Art		C
Communication Studies		C
Comp TIA A+		C
Construction		C
Construction Inspection	A	C
Construction Technology	A	C
Consumer/Family Studies		C
Drafting Technology	A	
Building Information Modeling (BIM)		C
Dassault Systems Solid Works		C
Mechanical Drafting		C
Tactile Mechanical Drafting		C
Environmental Control Technology	A	C
Air Condition Control Systems		C
ECT Air Conditioning, Heating and Refrigeration S.		C
Fashion		
Design	A	C
Merchandising	A	C
Fire Technology		
Certificate of Achievement	A	C
Skill Certificate		C
Food Services		
Advanced Skills		C
Basic Skills		C
Intermediate Skills		C
Graphic Design	A	C
Adobe Illustrator		C
Adobe InDesign		C
Adobe PhotoShop		C

A—Associate Degree Program C—Certificate Program

COLLEGE OF THE SEQUOIAS (continued)

Health		
Emergency Medical Technician B		C
Human Services (Social Work)	A	C
Nursing Assistant		C
Pharmacy Technician		C
Physical Therapist Assistant	A	
Registered Nursing	A	
Industrial Maintenance Technology	A	C
Electrician Training		C
Programmable Logic Controllers		C
Water and Waste Water Treatment		C
Welding	A	C
Plant Science		
Floral Technology		C
Landscape Design		C
Landscape Management	A	C
Ornamental Horticultural	A	C
Ornamental Horticultural, Retail Nursery Skills Options		C

A—Associate Degree Program C—Certificate Program

SHASTA COLLEGE

11555 Old Oregon Trail
P O Box 496006
Redding CA 94049-6006
530-242-7500
530-225-4990 Fax
www.shastacollege.edu

Semester System

Randall Meridith, Vice President of Instruction

Enrollment: Full-time 4,167 Part-time 5,858

Dormitories for men; Dormitories for women

OCCUPATIONAL PROGRAMS

Program	A	C
Administration of Justice	A	
Agriculture and Natural Resources		
Agricultural Business	A	
Agriculture Trades	A	
Equine Science	A	C
Equipment Operations and Maintenance		C
Forest Science and Technology	A	
Horticulture and Landscaping	A	C
Horticulture-Irrigation		C
Horticulture-Landscape and Turf Management		C
Horticulture-Retail Nursery Sales		C
Livestock Quality Assurance		C
Natural Resources	A	C
Pest Control Advisor Preparation		C
Sustainable Practices		C
Water/Waste Water Treatment		C
Watershed Restoration		C
Automotive Technology	A	C
Chassis		C
Electrical-Electronics		C
Engine Performance		C
Engine Repair		C
Heating-Air Conditioning		C
Powertrain		C
Business and Office Management		
Accounting	A	
Accounting Clerk/Bookkeeper		C
Administrative Office Assistant		C
Administrative Office Professional	A	C
Basic Business	A	
Business	A	
Business Retailing		C
Customer Service Academy		C
Entrepreneurship		C
Health Information Management	A	C
Management	A	
Office and Computer Technologies	A	
Computer and Information Systems		
Cisco Networking		C
Computer Maintenance		C
Network Administration	A	C
Systems Management	A	
Web Design		C
Windows Server		C
Education and Family		
Early Childhood Education	A	C
Family Child Care		C
Family Studies	A	
Human Development	A	
Life Management		C
Health Sciences and Nursing		
Dental Hygiene	A	
Nurse Aide/Home Health Aide		C
Nursing	A	
Vocation Nursing		C
Hospitality and Culinary Arts		
Baking		C
Bartender		C
Culinary Arts	A	C
Dietary Service Supervisor		C
Dining Room Management		C
Dining Room Staff		C
Food/Beverage/Lodging Management	A	
Line Cook		C
Hotel/Restaurant Management	A	C
Winemaking and Marketing		C
Geographic Information Systems	A	C
Fire Academy		
EMS–Emergency Medical Response	A	
Firefighter I		C
Firefighter II		C
Fire Investigation	A	
Fire Service Command, Company Office	A	
Fire Technology	A	
Public Safety and Services	A	
Wildland Fire Behavior	A	
Wildland Firefighter I Academy		C

A—Associate Degree Program C—Certificate Program

SIERRA COLLEGE

5000 Rocklin Rd
Rocklin CA 95677-3397
916-624-3333
www.sierracollege.edu

Darlene Jackson, Associate Dean, Business and Technology

Enrollment: Full-time 7,609 Part-time 13,079

Semester system; 8 week summer sessions

Dormitories for men; Dormitories for women

OCCUPATIONAL PROGRAMS

Administration of Justice		
Corrections	A	
Courts	A	
Law Enforcement	A	
Agriculture	A	C
Sustainable Agriculture	A	C
Sustainable Agriculture Business		C
Applied Art and Design		
Digital Illustration		C
Graphic Design	A	C
Illustration	A	C
Multimedia	A	C
Video Production and Editing		C
Visual Arts and Media		C
Web Design		C
Automotive Technology		
Air Conditioning & Body Electrical		C
Alignment and Brake		C
Automatic Transmission		C
Automotive Analysis	A	
Automotive Engine Machining		C
Emission and Driveability Tuneup		C
Entry Level Automotive Service and Repair		C
Master Automotive Technician		C
Power Train		C
Biological Sciences		
Watershed Ecology	A	C
Business		
Accounting	A	C
Administrative Professional	A	C
Business Administration	A	
Business Entrepreneurship	A	C
General Business	A	C
Management	A	C
Marketing	A	C
Real Estate	A	C
Small Business	A	C
Communication Studies		
General	A	
Graphic Design	A	
Mass Communication/Multimedia	A	
Computer Information Systems		
Computer Applications	A	C
Digital Literacy		C
Networking	A	C
Information Assurance Technician-Level 1,2		C
Technical Support	A	C
Virtual Office Professional–Administrative	A	C
Computer Science		
Computer Science	A	
Embedded Systems		C
Management Information Systems	A	
Web Programming		C
Construction and Energy Technology		
Energy Technology	A	
Photovoltaic		C
Photovoltaic Advanced		C
Residential Building Construction	A	C
Deaf Studies: American Sign Language	A	C
Drafting and Engineering Support		
Architectural/Civil	A	C
Architectural Drafting Specialist		C
Drafting Essentials		C
Mechanical/Civil	A	C
Mechanical Drafting Specialist		C
Engineering	A	
Civil Engineering Technology		C
General Engineering Technology		C
Environmental Studies and Sustainability	A	
Fashion		
Design		C
Industries	A	C
Merchandising		C
Fire Technology	A	C
Geographic Information Systems (GIS)		C
Human Development and Family	A	
Early Childhood Education	A	
Early Childhood Education–Associate Teacher		C
Early Childhood Education–Master Teacher	A	
Early Childhood Education–Site Supervisor	A	
Early Childhood Education–Teacher		C
Library Science		
Library Media Technician		C

A—Associate Degree Program C—Certificate Program

SIERRA COLLEGE (continued)

Mechatronics		
Electro-Mechanical		C
Mechatronics Technology		C
Nursing, Registered	A	
Nutrition and Fitness Trainer		C
Photography	A	C
Alternative Processes in Photography		C
Color Photography		C
Digital Imaging		C
Landscape Photography		C
Narrative Photography		C
Photographic Processes		C
Portrait, Fashion and Wedding Photography		C
Recreation Management	A	
Recreation Specialist		C
Theatre		
Costuming		C
Stagecraft		C
Theatre Arts	A	
Welding Technology	A	C
Gas Metal Arc Welding		C
Gas Tungsten Arc Welding		C
Metal Fabricator and Designer		C
Shielded Metal Arc Welding		C
Welding Entrepreneurship		C

A—Associate Degree Program C—Certificate Program

COLLEGE OF THE SISKIYOUS

800 College Ave
Weed CA 96094-2899
530-938-5555
530-938-5227 Fax
www.siskiyous.edu

Dr. Robert Taylor, Dean, Career & Technical Education

Semester system

Enrollment: Full-time 958 Part-time 2,067

Dormitories coed

OCCUPATIONAL PROGRAMS

Administration of Justice	A	
Level II, III Reserve Officer		C
Alcohol and Drug/Human Services	A	C
Business		
Accounting	A	C
Administrative Assistant	A	C
Business Administration	A	
Business Effectiveness		C
E-Business		C
Computer Science	A	
Game Design		C
PC Network/Hardware/Software		C
Programming		C
Web Design		C
Early Childhood Education	A	
Emergency Medical Technology-Paramedic	A	C
Fire/Emergency Response Technology	A	
Firefighter I, II		C
Fire Officer		C
Volunteer Firefighter		C
Wildland Fire Fighter Basic Training		C
Graphic Design		C
Nursing		
CNA-Certified Nurse Assistant		C
LVN-Licensed Vocational Nurse	A	C
LVN to RN Step-up	A	C
Power Generation Technology	A	C
Welding	A	
Advanced Level		C
Basic Level		C

A—Associate Degree Program C—Certificate Program

SKYLINE COLLEGE

3300 College Dr
San Bruno CA 94066-1698
650-738-4100
650-738-4338 Fax
www.skylinecollege.edu

Sandra Stefani Comerford, Vice President of Instruction

Enrollment: Full-time 3,307 Part-time 6,240

Semester system; 6 and 8 week summer sessions

No Housing

OCCUPATIONAL PROGRAMS

Accounting	A	C
Accounting Computer Specialist		C
Administration of Justice	A	C
After School Worker		C
Allied Health Science	A	
Emergency Medical Technology		C
Respiratory Therapy	A	
Surgical Technology	A	C
Surgical Technology: Central Service Tech with Clinical Practice	A	C
Automotive Technology	A	
Advanced Engine Performance Tech		C
Asian Engine Performance Tech		C
Automotive Entrepreneurship		C
Chassis Technology		C
Drive Train Technology		C
Electricity/Electronics		C
Engine Performance		C
Engines Technology		C
Entry Level		C
Biotechnology	A	
Business		
Air Freight Forwarding		C
Asian Business Practices		C
Business Administration		C
Business Management	A	C
Computer Information Specialist		C
Entrepreneurship		C
Entrepreneurship and Small Business Management		C
General Supervision		C
Import and Export		C
International Business		C
International Logistics	A	
International Logistics Customs Broker		C
International Trade	A	C
Legal Aspects of International Business		C
Legal Secretary	A	C
Multimedia Technology	A	C
Ocean Freight Forwarding		C
Office Assistant		C
Office Management	A	C
Warehouse Entry Level		C
Warehousing and Logistics		C
Cosmetology	A	C
Entrepreneurship		C
Esthetician		C
Massage Therapy		C
Dance	A	
Early Childhood Education	A	C
Early Intervention Assistant		C
Entrepreneurship		C
Foundations		C
Special Education		C
Family and Consumer Sciences	A	C
Fashion Merchandising	A	C
International Studies	A	
Journalism	A	C
Paralegal/Legal Assistant	A	C
Respiratory Therapy	A	
Solar Energy Technology		C
Solar Installation		C
Telecommunications and Network Information Technology		
Basic Networking		C
Network Engineering	A	C
PC Configuration & Repair		C
Wiring & Installation		C

A—Associate Degree Program C—Certificate Program

SOLANO COMMUNITY COLLEGE

4000 Suisun Valley Rd
Suisun CA 94585
707-864-7000
707-684-7175 Fax
www.solano.edu

Marie Morinee, Dean of School of Applied Technology and Business

Enrollment: Full-time 3,781 Part-time 8,103

Semester system, 6 to 8 week summer session

No Housing

OCCUPATIONAL PROGRAMS

Accounting	A	C
Account Clerk (Job-Direct)	A	C
General	A	C
Aeronautics	A	C
Airframe Maintenance Technician	A	C
Avionics Technician	A	C
Powerplant Maintenance Technician	A	C
Art	A	C
Graphic Design and Illustration	A	C
Automotive Body and Repair Technician	A	C
Banking and Finance, Bank Operation	A	C
Biotechnology-Industrial	A	C
Business	A	C
Insurance	A	C
Insurance Specialist	A	C
Child Development and Family Studies	A	C
Early Childhood Education	A	C
Communication Studies	A	C
Computer and Information Science	A	C
Computer Applications Specialist		C
Computer Programming	A	C
Database Specialist		C
Home-Based Computer Processor		C
Microcomputer Applications	A	C
Microsoft Office Master		C
Microsoft Office Specialist		C
Web Developer		C
Web Development and Administration	A	C
Web Programmer		C
Cosmetology	A	C
General	A	C
Nail Technician		C
Criminal Justice	A	C
Computer Forensics	A	C
Corrections	A	C
Law Enforcement	A	C
Drafting	A	C
Technician	A	C
Technology	A	C
Fashion Design	A	C
Film and Television	A	C
Fire Technology	A	C
Firefighter I Skills	A	C
General	A	C
Hazardous Substance Handling	A	C
Hazmat Worker		C
Pre-Fire Technician	A	C
Wild Land Fire Technician		C
Horticulture Science	A	C
Landscape Worker		C
Industrial Education	A	C
Industrial Management, Safety	A	C
Maintenance Technician	A	C
Manufacturing Technology		C
Journalism	A	C
Kinesiology	A	C
Fitness Professional		C
Physical Education	A	C
Management	A	C
General	A	C
Retail	A	C
Small Business	A	C
Marketing	A	C
Nursing	A	C
Office Technology	A	C
Administrative Assistant	A	C
General Office Assistant		C
Legal Office Assistant		C
Legal Specialist		C
Medical Office Assistant		C
Medical Office Specialist	A	C
Medical Transcription Specialist	A	C
Retail Clerk		C
Professional Photography	A	C
Real Estate	A	C
Theatre Arts	A	C
Water and Wastewater Technology	A	C
Welding	A	C
Equipment Operator		C
Industrial Technician	A	C
Welding Technician	A	C

A—Associate Degree Program C—Certificate Program

SOUTHWESTERN COLLEGE

900 Otay Lakes Rd
Chula Vista CA 91910-7299
619-421-6700
619-482-6323 Fax
www.swccd.edu

Dean, Business, Professional and Technical Education

Enrollment: Full-time 4,700 Part-time 10,500

Semester System; 6 or 9 week summer session

No Housing

OCCUPATIONAL PROGRAMS

Accounting	A	C
Administration of Justice	A	C
Corrections	A	C
Crime Scene Investigator	A	C
Forensics	A	C
Law Enforcement	A	C
Police Academy		C
Administrative Office Assistant–Bilingual		C
Architectural Technology	A	C
Advance		C
Automotive Technology	A	C
Brakes		C
Electrical/Electronic Systems		C
Engine Performance		C
Engine Repair		C
Heating and Air Conditioning		C
Manual Drive Train and Axles		C
Suspension and Steering		C
Transmission and Transaxle		C
Biotechnology	A	C
Business Administration	A	C
Finance		C
International Business		C
Management		C
Marketing		C
Business Management	A	
eBusiness	A	C
Entrepreneurship and Small Business	A	C
Financial and Investment		C
Child Development	A	
Child Development Teacher	A	C
Family Childcare–Bilingual		C
Spanish-to-English Associate Teacher		C
Community, Economic and Urban Developing	A	C
Intermediate		C
Computer Aided Design and Drafting (CAD)	A	C
Computer Information Systems	A	C
Applications Programming	A	C
Computer Programing with Emphasis on Applications	A	C
Internet	A	C
Internetwork Technician	A	C
Microcomputer Applications	A	C
Microcomputer Office and Technical Support Skills	A	C
Operations/PC Support Specialist	A	C
Systems Programming	A	C
Web Flash Developer and Gaming Animator	A	C
Web Shopping Cart Developer		C
Web Site Design and Developer	A	C
Web Site eCommerce Administrator	A	C
Computer Science	A	C
Construction Inspection	A	C
Construction Management	A	C
Culinary Arts–Cooking and Baking	A	C
Cooking Essentials		C
Professional Baking and Pastry		C
Dental Hygiene	A	
Design Technology	A	C
Electronics	A	C
Computer System Intensive Certification Training		C
Computer Technician		C
Emergency Medical Technician and Paramedic	A	C
Engineering	A	
Environmental Technology	A	
Environmental Management	A	C
Occupational Health & Safety	A	C
Event and Convention Planning	A	C
Exercise Science		
Fitness Specialist Certification		C
Fire Science	A	C
Geographic Information Science		C
Geospatial Technology Technician		C
Hospitality and Tourism Management		
Culinary Arts–Food Services Management	A	C
Event and Convention Management	A	C
Hotel Operations Management	A	C
Travel and Tourism Management	A	C
Insurance	A	C
International Business	A	C
Sales and Customer Service Professional		C
Journalism	A	

A—Associate Degree Program C—Certificate Program

SOUTHWESTERN COLLEGE (continued)

Landscape and Nursery Technology	A	C
Floral Design		C
Landscape Architecture	A	C
Landscape Operations	A	C
Golf and Sports Turf Management	A	C
Leadership and Supervision		C
Legal Office Professional	A	
Business Law Specialty		C
Civil Litigation Specialty		C
Criminal Law Specialty		C
Family Law Specialty		C
Legal Office Professional–Basic		C
Legal Office Professional–Bilingual	A	
Immigration Law Specialty		C
International Business Law Specialty		C
Legal Office Management	A	
Wills, Trusts, and Estates Specialty		C
Logistics and Transportation		C
International	A	
Medical Assistant		
Administrative	A	C
Basic		C
Clinical	A	C
Coding and Insurance		C
Intermediate		C
Office Management	A	C
Medical Laboratory Technician	A	
Medical Office Professional	A	
Music: Commercial	A	C
Nursing and Health Occupations	A	
Acute Care		C
Central Service Technology		C
Certified Nursing Assistant (CNA)		C
Nursing Vocational	A	C
Operating Room Nursing		C
Surgical Technology		C
Vocational	A	C
Office Information Systems (OIS)		
Professional	A	C
Professional–Bilingual	A	C
Microsoft Office Specialist		C
Office intensive Training–Bilingual	A	
Payroll Clerk		C
Paralegal Studies	A	C
Paralegal Studies–Bilingual	A	C
Pharmaceutical and Laboratory Science	A	C
Photography and Digital Imaging	A	
Graphic Applications		C
Professional Photography		C
Real Estate	A	C
Broker License		C
Salesperson License		C
Recording Arts and Technology	A	C
Surgical Technology	A	C
Sustainable Energy Studies		C
Sustainable Landscape Practices	A	
Telemedia	A	
Telemedia Production Specialist	A	C
Telemedia Technology	A	C
Theatre Arts–Performance	A	
Travel and Tourism	A	C
Virtual Business Professional	A	C
Office Support Professional		C

A—Associate Degree Program C—Certificate Program

TAFT COLLEGE

29 Cougar Ct
Taft CA 93268
661-763-7700
661-763-7705 Fax
www.taftcollege.edu

Semester system; 10 week summer session

Mark Williams, Vice President of Instruction

Enrollment: Full-time 976 Part-time 10,246

Coed dormitories

OCCUPATIONAL PROGRAMS

Accounting	A	C
Administration of Justice	A	
Corrections	A	C
Criminal Justice Administration	A	
Administrative Services	A	C
Administrative Services I		C
Administrative Services II		C
Microsoft Office Applications		C
Business Administration	A	
Court Reporting	A	C
Dental Hygiene	A	C
Direct Support Education	A	C
Early Care, Education and Family Studies	A	C
Assistant Teacher		C
Associate Teacher		C
Early Intervention Assistant I		C
Early Intervention Assistant II		C
Family Care Provider I and II		C
Master Teacher		C
Master Teacher Specializations		C
Teacher		C
Early Childhood Education	A	
Energy Technology	A	
Entry Level		C
Foundation		C
Field Tech		C
Industrial Health and Safety		C
Petroleum Engineering/Geological Tech		C
Engineering	A	
General Business	A	
Advanced Information Technology and Management		C
Information Technology and Management	A	C
Management	A	C
Management Customer Service		C
Industrial Health and Safety	A	
Entry Level Hazardous Material		C
Foundation		C
Midlevel		C
Petroleum Technology Well Control and Drilling I-IV		C
Welding Technology	A	
Gas Metal Arc and Flux Core Arc Welding		C
Gas Tungsten Arc Welding		C
Pipe Code Welding		C
Structural Code Welding		C
Welding Assistant/Helper		C

A—Associate Degree Program C—Certificate Program

VENTURA COLLEGE

4667 Telegraph Rd
Ventura CA 93003
805-289-6400
805-289-8971 Fax
www.venturacollege.edu

Dr. Kathleen Schrader, Dean of Career and Technical Education

Enrollment: Full-time 4,546 Part-time 8,443

Semester system, 4, 6, 7, & 8 week summer sessions

No Housing

OCCUPATIONAL PROGRAMS

Administrative Assistant	A	C
Agriculture	A	
Automotive	A	C
Biotechnology		C
Business	A	C
Business Management	A	C
Child Development	A	C
Computer Science	A	C
Construction Technology	A	C
Criminal Justice	A	C
Development Studies		C
Drafting	A	C
Economics		C
Emergency Medical Technology		C
Engineering Technology	A	C
Environmental Science & Resource Management		C
Geographic Information Systems (GIS)		C
Health Information Technology		C
Health Sciences Administration		C
Holistic Studies	A	
Human Services	A	C
International Studies	A	C
Journalism	A	C
Leadership		C
Manufacturing Technology		C
Medical Assistant–Administrative	A	C
Medical Assistant–Multi-Skilled	A	C
Multimedia	A	C
Nursing Science	A	C
Paramedic	A	C
Photography	A	C
Sign Language		C
Supervision	A	C
Theatre Arts	A	C
Water Science	A	C
Welding	A	C

A—Associate Degree Program C—Certificate Program

VICTOR VALLEY COLLEGE

18422 Bear Valley Rd
Victorville CA 92395-5849
760-245-4271
760-241-0881 Fax
www.vvc.edu

Semester System; 6, 8 week summer sessions

Patricia Luther, MSN, Ed.D., Dean of Health Science, Public Safety and Industrial Technology

Enrollment: Full-time & Part-time 10,678

No Housing

OCCUPATIONAL PROGRAMS

Program		
Administration of Justice	A	C
Correctional Science		C
Corrections		C
Fingerprint Recognition and Classification		C
Forensic		C
Forensic Specialist		C
Juvenile Counselor Course		C
Law Enforcement Modulated Course		C
Module A Reserve Academy Firearms Only		C
PC 832 Law Enforcement Course		C
Police Technician Specialist		C
School Police Course: PC 832.3		C
Agriculture and Natural Resources		
Animal Science Technician		C
Ecological Restoration Technician		C
Environmental Field Studies		C
Equine Science Specialist		C
Floral Design		C
Geospatial Technician		C
Horticulture & Landscape Technician		C
Horticulture Specialist		C
Landscape Irrigation		C
Landscape Specialist		C
Mojave Desert Master Gardener		C
Natural Resource Management Technician		C
Allied Health		
Certified Phlebotomy Technician		C
Nursing Assistant/Home Health Aide		C
Automotive Technology	A	
Automotive Brake and Suspension Specialist		C
Automotive Drivability Specialist		C
Automotive Inspection & Maintenance Technician		C
Automotive Repair Shop Manager		C
Automotive Specialist I	A	C
Automotive Specialist II	A	C
Automotive Technician	A	C
Automotive Transmission Specialist		C
Automotive Window Tinting Technician		C
Basic Inspection Area Smog Technician		C
Collision Repair Technician		C
Automotive Technology (continued)		
Engine Machinist Specialist		C
Enhanced Inspection Area Smog Technician		C
Heavy Duty Diesel Truck Lubrication and Inspection Specialist		C
Heavy Duty Truck Brake Repair Specialist		C
Import Sport Tuning and Customization		C
Motorcycle Repair Technician		C
Recreational Vehicle Service and Repair Technician		C
Small Engine Repair Specialist		C
Aviation		
Airframe–Aviation Maintenance Technology		C
General Aviation Maintenance Technology		C
Powerplant–Maintenance Technology		C
Biotechnology		C
Business	A	
Business Administration	A	
Bookkeeping		C
Management		C
Business Education Technologies	A	
Administrative Assistant		C
Computer Systems		C
Data Typist		C
Legal Office		C
Medical Office		C
Office Services		C
Spreadsheet Processor		C
Word Processor		C
Business Real Estate and Escrow	A	
Advanced Business Real Estate		C
Basic Business Real Estate		C
Business Real Estate Apprentice		C
Business Real Estate Trainee		C
Escrow Secretarial Services		C
Property Management		C
Real Estate Appraiser		C
Real Estate Escrow		C
Real Estate Marketing		C
Real Estate Secretarial Services		C

A—Associate Degree Program C—Certificate Program

VICTOR VALLEY COLLEGE (continued)

Program	A	C
Child Development	A	
Family Child Care		C
Principles of Early Childhood Education		C
Level I: Associate Teacher		
Level II: Teacher		
Level III: Supervisor		
Computer Information Systems		
Database Administration		C
My SQL Database Developer		C
Netware		C
Network Specialist		C
Productivity Software Specialist		C
Programming		C
UNIX Administrator		C
Visual Basic Programming		C
Web Authoring		C
Computer Integrated Design and Graphics	A	
Architectural CADD Technical I		C
CADD Technician I		C
Civil CADD Technical I		C
Computer Animation Technician I		C
Digital Animation Artist		C
Digital Animation Technician I-3ds Max		C
Digital Animation Technician I-Softimage XSI		C
Drafting Technician		C
Geographical Information Systems (GIS)		C
Visual Communications Graphic Design		C
Visual Communications Print Production		C
Construction and Manufacturing Technology	A	
Basic Electrical Technician		C
Basic HVAC/R		C
Basic Residential Maintenance Technician		C
Basic Woodworking		C
Building Construction		C
Building Inspection		C
Construction Management		C
Construction Technology		C
Plumbing Technician		C
Public Works		C
Renewable Energy		C
Educational Technology		C
Electronics and Computer Technology	A	
A+ Certification Examination Preparation		C
CISCO Networking Academy I, II, III, IV, V, VI, VII		C
Communication Electronics		C
Computer Technology		C
Digital Electronics		C
Electronics Technology		C
Fiber Optic Cabling Technician		C
N+ Certification Examination Preparation		C
Network Cabling Technician Technology		C
Wireless Communication Technology		C
Wireless MSCSE Examination Preparation		C
Electronics Engineering Technology	A	C
Emergency Medical Technician		
Emergency Medical Technician I (Ambulance)		C
Emergency Medical Technician (Refresher)		
Fire Technology	A	
Fire Company Officer		C
Fire Fighter		C
Fire Prevention Officer		C
Journalism	A	C
Media Arts		
Digital Animation Artist		C
Digital Animation Technician I-3ds Max		C
Digital Animation Technician I-Softimage XSI		C
Medical Assistant	A	C
Nursing	A	
Associate Degree Nursing		C
Nursing Licensure		C
Ornamental Horticulture	A	
Paralegal Studies		C
Paramedic	A	C
Photography		
Digital Photography		C
Political Science		
International Studies		C
Respiratory Therapy	A	C
Restaurant Management	A	C
Welding	A	C

A—Associate Degree Program C—Certificate Program

WEST HILLS COLLEGE COALINGA

300 Cherry Lane
Coalinga CA 93210-1399
559-934-2000
559-935-3788 Fax
www.westhillscollege.com

Semester system, Summer Session

Raquel Rodriguez, Associate Dean of Student Learning

Enrollment: Full-time 606 Part-time 1,326

Dormitories

OCCUPATIONAL PROGRAMS

Administration of Justice		
Corrections	A	
Law Enforcement	A	
Agriculture Science Technology	A	C
Precision Agriculture		C
Agricultural Maintenance Mechanic		C
Business		
Bookkeeping	A	C
Business Management	A	C
Retail Business Management	A	C
Business Administration	A	
Child Development		
Administration		C
Care and Education	A	C
Early Intervention Assistant		C
Family Day Care		C
Computer Information Systems	A	C
Heavy Equipment Operation		C
Hospital Peace Officer		C
Kinesiology	A	
Nurse Assistant		C
Office Management and Technology	A	C
Clerk Typist	A	C
Secretary/Word Processing	A	C
Performing Arts	A	
Technical Theatre Production		C
Television Production		C
Psychiatric Technician	A	C

A—Associate Degree Program C—Certificate Program

WEST HILLS COLLEGE LEMOORE

555 College Ave
Lemoore CA 93245
559-925-3000
559-924-8065 Fax
www.westhillscollege.com./lemoore

Semester system, 6 week summer sessions

James Preston, Dean of Educational Services

Enrollment: Full-time 1,369 Part-time 2,872

No Housing

OCCUPATIONAL PROGRAMS

Administration of Justice		
Corrections	A	
Law Enforcement	A	
Business		
Bookkeeping	A	C
Management	A	C
Retail Business Management	A	C
Business Administration	A	
Business–Entrepreneurship		C
Business Office Technologies	A	C
Child Development	A	C
Administrative		C
Assistant Teacher Level		C
Associate Teacher Level		C
Early Intervention Assistant		C
Family Day Care		C
Teacher Level		C
Computer Information Systems	A	C
Hospitality, Restaurant and Casino Management	A	
Casino Management		C
Chef Apprentice		C
Hotel Management		C
Restaurant Management		C
Human Services		C
Eligibility Worker		C
Mental Health		C
Social Work Assistant		C
Substance Abuse Specialist		C
Youth Worker		C
Nursing	A	
LVN to Nursing (RN)	A	C
PT to Nursing	A	
Paramedic	A	C

A—Associate Degree Program C—Certificate Program

WEST LOS ANGELES COLLEGE

9000 Overland Ave
Culver City CA 90230-3500
310-287-4200
310-841-0396 Fax
www.wlac.edu

Robert Sprague, Vice President of Academic Affairs
Aracely Aguiar, Dean of Career & Technical Education
Walter Jones, Dean of Academic Affairs

Enrollment: Full-time 3,305; Part-time 8,292

Semester system; One 5 week winter session, Two 6 week and two 8 week summer sessions. Two 8 week sessions per semester in certain programs

No Housing

OCCUPATIONAL PROGRAMS

Program	A	C
Administration of Justice	A	
Alcohol Drug Studies	A	C
Corrections and Probation Officer		C
Allied Health		
Certified Nurse Assistant		C
Dental Hygiene	A	
Home Health Aide		C
Medical Assistant, Administrative	A	C
Medical Assistant, Clinical		C
American Sign Language		C
Architecture		C
Aviation Technology		
Aircraft Powerplant Technician		C
Airframe Maintenance Technician	A	C
Aviation Maintenance Technician	A	
Business	A	C
Accounting	A	C
Administration	A	
Child Development	A	C
Computer Science and Application		
Business Application and Database		C
Legal Secretary		C
Word Processing	A	C
Computer Science Information	A	C
CISCO Network		C
Computer Network and Management	A	C
Web Support and Database	A	C
Fire Technology	A	C
Management		
Small Business	A	C
Marketing	A	C
Media Arts		
Broadcasting		C
Cinema		C
Film Production Crafts		C
Theater Arts		C
Paralegal Studies	A	C
Physical Education		C
Real Estate	A	C
Travel and Hospitality		
Hospitality	A	C
Travel	A	C

A—Associate Degree Program C—Certificate Program

WEST VALLEY COLLEGE

14000 Fruitvale Ave
Saratoga CA 95070-5698
408-741-2098
408-741-2671 Fax
www.westvalley.edu

Brad Weisberg, Dean, Career Education & Workforce Development

Enrollment: Full-time & Part-time 11,000

Semester system; 4, 6, and 8 week summer sessions

No Housing

OCCUPATIONAL PROGRAMS

Program	A	C
Accounting Clerk		C
Administration of Justice	A	
Architecture	A	C
Art	A	
Computer Arts: Animation	A	C
Business/Business Administration	A	
Administrative Management		C
Business–Administration		C
Business–Communications		C
Business–Leadership Skills		C
Business Management		C
Human Relations in Business		C
International Foreign Language		C
Marketing		C
Professional Selling		C
Project Management		C
Retail Management		C
Small Business Startup		C
Child Studies		
Communication and the Arts Specialization		C
Early Childhood Education	A	C
Early Intervention		C
Program Director Specialization		C
Computer Applications	A	C
Office Technologies–Level I and II		C
Office Technologies–Online		C
Computer Information Systems		
Computer Science Option		C
Court Reporting and Related Technologies	A	C
Legal Secretarial Studies		C
Legal Transcription Technologist	A	C
Note Reading and Scoping Technologist		C
Office Assistant/Transcription Technologist		C
Digital Media/Internet Services		
Graphic Design		C
Web and Mobile Design	A	C
Engineering	A	
Fashion Design/Apparel Technology		
Apparel Design–Level I and II	A	C
Apparel Production–Level I and II	A	C
Health Care Technologies		
Clinic Assistant		C
Insurance Billing Specialist		C
Massage Therapy		C
Medical Administrative Assistant		C
Medical Assistant	A	C
Medical Office Reception		C
Orthopedic Technician		C
Interior Design	A	C
Advanced Interior Design		C
Computer Aided Drafting/Design		C
Facilities Planning and Design		C
Interior Restoration and Preservation		C
Kitchen and Bath Design		C
Landscape Architecture	A	C
Paralegal	A	C
Park Management	A	C
Geographic Information Science		C
Physical Education	A	
Dance Specialist		C
Exercise Science/Sports Medicine		C
Theatre Arts	A	
Acting Emphasis	A	
Costume/Makeup Emphasis	A	
Film Studies	A	
Stage Technology	A	
Video/Film	A	

A—Associate Degree Program C—Certificate Program

WOODLAND COMMUNITY COLLEGE

2300 E. Gibson Rd
Woodland CA 95776
530-661-5700
530-661-5705 Fax
http://wcc.yccd.edu

Al Konuwa DPA, Vice President for Academic and Student Services

Enrollment: 4,000

Semester system

No Housing

OCCUPATIONAL PROGRAMS

Administration of Justice	A	
Corrections	A	
Law Enforcement	A	
Agriculture		
Agriculture	A	
Agricultural Business	A	C
Environmental Horticulture	A	C
Landscape Design		C
Landscape Installation and Maintenance		C
Sustainable Agriculture		C
Business		
Accounting	A	C
Business Administration	A	
Business Computer Applications	A	C
General Business Management	A	
Income Tax Preparation	A	C
Personnel Management	A	
Small Business Management	A	C
Small Business Management–Entrepreneurship		C
Digital Media		C
Early Childhood Education		
Child Development Associate Teacher		C
Child Development Teacher		C
Diversity in Early Childhood Education		C
Early Childhood Education	A	
Infant and Toddler		C
School Age Children		C
Human Services		
Chemical Dependency Awareness	A	C
Chemical Dependency Counselor	A	C
Human Services	A	

A—Associate Degree Program C—Certificate Program

YUBA COLLEGE

2088 N Beale Rd
Marysville CA 95901-7605
530-741-6700
530-634-7709 Fax
www.yc.yccd.edu

Semester system; Summer session

Edward Davis, Dean, Business/Social Secience

Enrollment: Full-time 3,664 Part-time 5,668

No Housing

OCCUPATIONAL PROGRAMS

Administration of Justice		
Basic Police Academy	A	C
Basic Requalification		C
Correctional Officer Academy		C
Corrections	A	
Juvenile Counselor Academy		C
Law Enforcement	A	
Peace Officer Orientation		C
Reserve Training Module I		C
Reserve Training Module II		C
Reserve Training Module III		C
Specialized Investigator Academy		C
Agriculture and Plant Science		
Agricultural Business		C
Environmental Horticulture	A	C
Architectural Studies	A	C
Art	A	
Commercial Art	A	
Photographic Imaging	A	C
Automotive Technology		
Auto Body and Repair	A	C
Automatic Transmission/Transaxle		C
Body Repair		C
Brakes		C
Drive Trains	A	C
Electrical Systems		C
Engine Machining		C
Engine Performance		C
Engine Repair		C
Heating and Air Conditioning		C
Manual Drive Train and Axles		C
Master Mechanic	A	C
Suspension and Steering		C
Tune-up and Driveability	A	C
Business		
Accounting	A	C
Administrative Assistant	A	C
Business Administration	A	
Business Computer Applications	A	C
General Business Management	A	C
Income Tax Preparation	A	C
Information Technologies	A	
Legal Office Skills	A	C
Medical Office Skills	A	C
Personnel Management	A	C
Retail Management		C
Small Business Management	A	C
Word Processing	A	C
Computer Science	A	C
Cosmetology	A	C
Culinary Arts	A	C
Early Childhood Education	A	
Child Development Teacher		C
Diversity Specialization		C
Infant and Toddler		C
Pediatric First Aid/CPR		C
School Age Specialization		C
Emergency Medical Technician		
EMT-1		C
EMT-1 Refresher		C
Fire Technology	A	C
Fire Academy	A	C
Firefighter Academy		C
Fire Technology Practicum I		C
Fire Technology Practicum II		C
First Responder		C
Human Services	A	
Chemical Dependency Counselor	A	C
Manufacturing Technology – Machining	A	C
Mass Communications	A	C
Nursing		
Associate Degree Nursing	A	
Psychiatric Technology	A	
Radiologic Technology	A	
Veterinary Technician	A	
Laboratory Animal Medicine		C
Large Animal Care and Management		C
Shelter Medicine		C
Veterinary Public Health and Food Safety		C
Veterinary Receptionist/Assistant		C
Welding Technologies	A	C

A—Associate Degree Program C—Certificate Program

SECTION 4
Index to College Programs

Program titles are listed. Most are cross-referenced to the Program Location Charts in Section 2. Special programs are referenced to the college pages where they are listed.

SECTION 4
INDEX TO COLLEGE PROGRAMS

Boldfaced entries with page numbers are headings that will be found on pages 6 to 31. Other entries refer you to one of these headings. Entries for **specialized programs** refer you to the college that has the programs.

CALIFORNIA COMMUNITY COLLEGE CAMPUSES

SAN FRANCISCO BAY AREA

Alameda
Berkeley City
Cañada
Chabot
Contra Costa
De Anza
Diablo
Evergreen
Foothill
Laney
Las Positas
Los Medanos
Marin
Merritt
Mission
Napa
Ohlone
San Francisco City
San Jose City
San Mateo
Santa Rosa
Skyline
Solano
West Valley

LOS ANGELES AREA

Cerritos
Citrus
Coastline
Cypress
East Los Angeles
El Camino
Fullerton
Glendale
Golden West
Long Beach City
Los Angeles City
Los Angeles Harbor
Los Angeles Mission
Los Angeles Pierce
Los Angeles Southwest
Los Angeles Trade-Tech.
Lost Angeles Valley
Mt. San Antonio
Orange Coast
Pasadena City
Rio Hondo
Santa Ana
Santa Monica
Santiago Canyon
West Los Angeles

COLLEGE, LOCATION, AND PHONE NUMBER

Access college websites from www.cccco.edu

Alameda	Alameda	510-522-7221
Allan Hancock	Santa Maria	805-922-6966
American River	Sacramento	916-484-8011
Antelope Valley	Lancaster	661-772-6300
Bakersfield	Bakersfield	661-395-4011
Barstow	Barstow	760-252-2411
Berkeley City	Berkeley	510-981-2800
Butte	Oroville	530-895-2511
Cabrillo	Aptos	831-479-6201
Cañada	Redwood City	650-306-3100
Canyons	Santa Clarita	661-259-7800
Cerritos	Norwalk	562-860-2451
Cerro Coso	Ridgecrest	760-384-6100
Chabot	Hayward	510-723-6600
Chaffey	Rancho Cucamonga	909-652-6000
Citrus	Glendora	626-852-6402
Coastline	Fountain Valley	714-546-7600
Columbia	Sonora	209-588-5100
Contra Costa	San Pablo	510-235-7800
Copper Mountain	Joshua Tree	760-366-3791
Cosumnes River	Sacramento	916-691-7344
Crafton Hills	Yucaipa	909-794-2161
Cuesta	San Luis Obispo	805-546-3973
Cuyamaca	El Cajon	619-660-4000
Cypress	Cypress	714-484-7000
De Anza	Cupertino	408-864-5678
Desert	Palm Desert	760-773-2571
Diablo Valley	Pleasant Hill	925-685-1230
East Los Angeles	Monterey Park	323-265-8973
El Camino	Torrance	310-532-3670
Evergreen Valley	San Jose	408-274-7900
Feather River	Quincy	530-283-0202
Folsom Lake	Folsom	916-608-6500
Foothill	Los Altos Hills	650-949-7777
Fresno City	Fresno	559-442-4600
Fullerton	Fullerton	714-992-7000
Gavilan	Gilroy	408-848-4800
Glendale	Glendale	818-240-1000
Golden West	Huntington Beach	714-892-7711
Grossmont	El Cajon	619-644-7000
Hartnell	Salinas	831-755-6960
Imperial Valley	Imperial	760-355-6217
Irvine Valley	Irvine	949-451-5100
Lake Tahoe	South Lake Tahoe	530-541-4660
Laney	Oakland	510-834-5740
Las Positas	Livermore	925-424-1000
Lassen	Susanville	530-257-6181
Long Beach City	Long Beach	562-938-4111
Los Angeles City	Los Angeles	323-953-4000
Los Angeles Harbor	Wilmington	310-233-4042
Los Angeles Mission	Sylmar	818-364-7600
Los Angeles Pierce	Woodland Hills	818-347-0551
Los Angeles Southwest	Los Angeles	323-241-5225
L.A.Trade-Tech	Los Angeles	213-763-7000
Los Angeles Valley	Van Nuys	818-947-2600
Los Medanos	Pittsburg	925-439-2181
Marin	Kentfield	415-457-8811
Mendocino	Ukiah	707-468-3002
Merced	Merced	209-384-6000
Merritt	Oakland	510-531-4911
MiraCosta	Oceanside	760-757-2121
Mission	Santa Clara	408-988-2200
Modesto	Modesto	209-575-6058
Monterey Peninsula	Monterey	831-646-4000
Moorpark	Moorpark	805-378-1400
Moreno Valley	Moreno Valley	951-571-6100
Mt. San Antonio	Walnut	909-594-5611
Mt. San Jacinto	San Jacinto	951-487-6752
Napa	Napa	707-253-3000
Norco	Norco	951-372-7000
Ohlone	Fremont	510-659-6202
Orange Coast	Costa Mesa	714-432-5072
Oxnard	Oxnard	805-986-5800
Palomar	San Marcos	760-744-1150
Palo Verde	Blythe	760-921-5500
Pasadena City	Pasadena	626-585-7123
Porterville	Porterville	559-791-2200
Redwoods	Eureka	707-476-4100
Reedley	Reedley	559-638-3641
Rio Hondo	Whittier	562-692-0921
Riverside	Riverside	951-222-8490
Sacramento City	Sacramento	916-558-2568
Saddleback	Mission Viejo	949-582-4500
San Bernardino Valley	San Bernardino	909-384-4400
San Diego City	San Diego	619-388-3400
San Diego Mesa	San Diego	619-388-2600
San Diego Miramar	San Diego	619-388-7800
San Francisco City	San Francisco	415-550-4440
San Joaquin Delta	Stockton	209-954-5151
San Jose City	San Jose	408-298-2181
San Mateo	San Mateo	650-574-6161
Santa Ana	Santa Ana	714-564-6000
Santa Barbara City	Santa Barbara	805-965-0581
Santa Monica	Santa Monica	310-434-4000
Santa Rosa	Santa Rosa	707-527-4011
Santiago Canyon	Orange	714-628-4900
Sequoias	Visalia	559-730-3700
Shasta	Redding	530-242-7500
Sierra	Rocklin	916-624-3333
Siskiyous	Weed	530-938-5555
Skyline	San Bruno	650-738-4100
Solano	Suisun	707-864-7000
Southwestern	Chula Vista	619-421-6700
Taft	Taft	661-763-7700
Ventura	Ventura	805-654-6400
Victor Valley	Victorville	760-245-4271
West Hills Coalinga	Coalinga	559-934-2000
West Hills Lemoore	Lemoore	559-925-3000
West Los Angeles	Culver City	310-287-4200
West Valley	Saratoga	408-741-2098
Woodland	Woodland	530-661-5700
Yuba	Marysville	530-741-6700